Conn was deliberately taking over her life

"I am *not* your possession!" Luce protested hotly.

Conn smiled and pulled her down onto his knees, holding her until she stopped struggling. "Perhaps not yet, but it won't be long before you are. You're not stupid; you know I want you."

"Don't my wishes count for anything?"

A black brow lifted. "We both knew, right from the moment we set eyes on each other, that this is where we were headed."

His fingers threaded gently through her hair. And although she knew he was wrong, Luce shivered and turned her flushed face into the strong column of his throat.

His deep voice said quietly, "You come to life when I touch you, Luce. Don't try to lie to me."

ROBYN DONALD

the dark abyss

Harlequin Books

TORONTO · LONDON · LOS ANGELES · AMSTERDAM
SYDNEY · HAMBURG · PARIS · STOCKHOLM · ATHENS · TOKYO

Harlequin Presents edition published May 1982
ISBN 0-373-10500-2

Original hardcover edition published in 1981
by Mills & Boon Limited

CHAPTER ONE

'YOU should have come, Luce! The film was marvellous, and oh, Dean Parr is the most gorgeous actor I've ever seen!'

Luce Laurenson looked up, smiling, and went across the room to switch off the television.

'Was it as good as the play was supposed to be? That got rave reviews and had a terrifically long run, didn't it?'

The taller of the two women who had come into the living room of the flat they all shared smiled as she sank into a chair, slipping her shoes from her feet. 'It was magnificent. The acting was super, and Teresa's right, Dean Parr was an ideal hero.' She flashed a humorous glance at her companion. 'He died beautifully, and Teresa wept buckets. Sitting next to her at a sad film is like keeping company with a herd of whales, all spouting with great feeling.'

Teresa Halliday grinned, totally unrepentant. 'Even you got all misty-eyed at the end, Faith, so don't pretend to be so hard-boiled. I think everybody cried; it was like a Greek play or one of Shakespeare's tragedies—cathartic. I noticed several men looking furtive as they blew their noses.'

'Just the thing for a warm spring Saturday night in Whangarei.' Luce Laurenson was English, her clipped speech at variance with the New Zealand drawl of her companions. She had typical English colouring, or perhaps Nordic was a better description, with silver hair and eyes of that peculiarly clear cloud grey so rarely seen in the Antipodes. Set in dark lashes and brows, they were the main features of a face which lacked true beauty of feature yet possessed a compelling attraction, the pallor of it relieved by a mouth that had a curiously disciplined line.

As she moved gracefully around the tiny kitchenette making coffee she listened to her companions' conversation with a half-smile curving her lips. Not for the first time she thought how lucky she was to be sharing the flat with two such women, kindly, practical Faith and the more lively Teresa with her keen sense of humour and ardent appreciation of life.

'I'm glad you enjoyed it,' Luce said now, setting out pottery mugs. 'Who did the screenplay?'

'I looked specially,' Faith answered. 'It was the chap who wrote the original play—Conn Ramsay.'

Luce frowned, chasing an elusive memory. 'Conn Ramsay?' she murmured. 'It—the name sounds familiar.'

Her companions avoided looking at her or each other. After a moment Faith took her coffee, saying as she did so, 'He is famous, of course. He wrote one play set in the Middle Ages, about a band of lepers. They did it on T.V., remember?'

'I remember,' Teresa responded, shivering slightly. 'It was gruesome.'

'Very strong stuff.' Faith's voice was dry. 'The man's a cynic, but there's always a tiny ray of hope left at the end of his plays. He's written quite a few, each one a bigger hit than the last. The critics don't compare him with Shakespeare like our rash young friend here, but you get the feeling that they would if William S. wasn't sacred.'

'I've probably read about him somewhere.' Luce sank into a chair. 'Did you see anyone you know?'

'Jolie Stewart, with an absolutely gorgeous man in tow.' Teresa grinned wickedly. 'At least, he wasn't in tow, she was. All blatant eyelash-fluttering and coy lip-licking, but I don't think it was having the usual effect.'

Luce chuckled. 'I get the impression you don't like Jolie much. Did she steal one of your boy-friends once?'

'When we were at primary school, but that's not why I can't stand her. She's a snob, she's rapidly driving her mother round the bend with her antics, and Mrs Stewart is a darling.' Teresa sipped her coffee, then added slyly, 'She sets my teeth on edge. She's always given the impression that she thinks she's got all of Northland's share of sex appeal in her own rather too generously endowed form.'

One of Luce's brows lifted in comical interrogation. 'Miaow! Didn't she introduce you?'

Both of her companions burst into laughter; Teresa sobered, saying wryly, 'You know me too well, but honestly, Luce, it *was* funny. She was obviously dithering between showing him off and basking in every woman's envy, or keeping him unobtrusive in case someone pinched him.'

'The amusing part being that he stood there listening to her with a kind of bored amusement that would have had me cringing if I'd been with him,' Faith commented. 'He doesn't suffer fools gladly.'

'What was he like? To look at, I mean?' Luce was curious. Jolie Stewart was a stunning beauty. Most men never got past the perfect physical shell to discover the not particularly pleasant personality beneath it.

'Oh, dark; dark hair, not quite black, very tanned skin. Harsh features—a clever face. Eyes which saw everything. His expression didn't give much away, but his mouth—well, that still gives me goosebumps.' Teresa gave a mock shudder, pronouncing, 'Very sensual, that mouth. In fact, he gave an overpowering impression of fabulous male, all brooding intensity and what Faith in her youth used to call "animal magnetism".'

'Never used the expression,' Faith protested, smiling as she set her empty coffee mug back on the bench. 'Have you a headache, Luce? You look a bit shadowy around the eyes.'

'Yes, nurse,' Luce smiled. 'Only a vague one, though; I very rarely get them now.'

'Well, off to bed, then. Tomorrow, thank heavens, we'll all be able to relax. What say we go to the beach? If the weather's fine, of course.'

The weather was fine, after a somewhat subdued start to the day. By mid-morning the warm spring sun had banished the clouds and what little breeze there was whispered gently in from the North, bringing with it a hint of the tropics.

'Just the day for acquiring an early tan,' Teresa decided as she loaded the hamper into the boot of Faith's small, rather elderly car. 'Everybody got everything? O.K., let's away, folks.'

They had decided to go to Waipu Cove, a long surf beach south of Whangarei several miles from the small village of Waipu where over a hundred years ago a brave band of pioneers had settled after a hair-raising voyage from Nova Scotia in boats they had built for themselves.

Luce looked around with eager eyes. The winter had been wet and miserable and this was the first time she had really felt the spring. Along the streams kowhai trees bore golden offerings to the sun and in the lush paddocks there were lambs and calves playing beside their mothers. The air was soft and warm with promise, every farmhouse garden gay with flowers. Beside the road the manuka bloomed, starry white blossoms honey-scented against the grey-green foliage of the bushes.

New Zealand was lovely, she thought wistfully. So lovely. The two years she had spent here had been very happy ones. No one could be kinder or more fun than Teresa and Faith, and because of their friendship she had a wide and interesting circle of acquaintances. She enjoyed working in the antique shop. Her life was very pleasant.

'Bring your bikini, Luce?'

She smiled and nodded at Teresa. 'Yes, why?'

'Oh, just that it looks lovely on you. I've brought mine too. I'm determined to get some tan before Greg comes back.' Artlessly Teresa lifted her hand to look at the diamonds her fiancé had given her. 'I miss him like hell!'

'Another six months.' Faith turned the wheel to take the side road to the beach. 'Then another year and you'll be married. He's all set to join his father in his practice, isn't he?'

'Yes. Oh, I wish time would hurry!'

'It goes fast enough for me,' Faith commented. 'How about you, Luce?'

'Fast enough indeed. People are already starting to buy stuff for Christmas presents, and I feel as though I haven't recovered from last year's summer rush.' But she didn't say that, for her time seemed to flow like a circle, no beginning, no end.

The warm day had brought out plenty of picnic parties along the beach, most of them family groups, but there were enough couples to give the long sweep of sand a frivolous air. Because of her pale skin Luce anointed herself with a sun-block before stretching out on her towel. Teresa joined her in her sun-worship, but Faith sheltered beneath a large hat and read a book.

After a while she interrupted Teresa's careful timing of their exposure to murmur softly, 'Don't look now, but there's Jolie. Plus the handsome brute.'

'My, my, aren't we making the most of our charms!' Teresa sighed. 'Oh dear, that girl brings out the worst in me. I'm going to *make* her introduce him.'

'Teresa!' But Luce had to watch as Teresa sprang to her feet and with mock girlishness, waved, calling, 'Jolie! Jolie Stewart!'

Jolie was forced to swerve towards them. Her expression set in lines of extreme petulance as she spoke rapidly to the man beside her. Jolie's normal habit was to clutch one arm of her escort, but it appeared that she was too intimidated by this companion to drape herself over him.

Luce sat up, reaching for her jacket, her eyes behind

the sunglasses wide and frightened. He looked ... *familiar*! She was almost sure that she knew the exact dark green which shaded his eyes. And the smile, that derisive, hard movement of his lips—surely she had seen him smile like that before, and been hurt by it.

As they approached she huddled into her wrap, pulling the belt tightly around her slender waist. A tide of excitement rose hot within her, but she forced it down, aware that to concentrate now might make any returning memory depart irretrievably.

Jolie put off her air of sulkiness as she introduced him. Although he gave no indication that he knew Luce she felt that cold inimical glance on her for minutes afterwards. It was no surprise when she heard that his name was Conn Ramsay.

'The playwright?' Teresa exclaimed.

He looked down at her, a quizzical smile softening the lines of his mouth. 'The very same. Didn't I see you at the film last night?'

'If you didn't see her you almost certainly heard her,' Faith told him drily, her glance very level and direct. 'She was one of the weepers. The gusty one.'

He grinned at that, summing her up in turn. 'I'm always pleased when my work moves anyone to tears. A very definite ego-booster.' The cool glance moved across to rest on Luce's partly averted face. 'You weren't there, miss—Luce?'

'No.' She was fully in control of herself once more and although she knew that she was being too abrupt she could see no reason for giving any explanation.

So there was an awkward little silence until Jolie said, 'Well, perhaps we'd better move on, Conn.'

'Are we in any hurry?'

That was all that he said, but Jolie flushed and for some strange reason Luce felt sorry for her.

'No, of course we're not,' the older girl said gaily, unconvincingly, her eyes behind the fashionably enormous sunglasses fixed on to his face with painful intensity.

'Sit down,' Faith invited. 'Luce, you're closest to the hamper; how about getting us out something to drink? It's hot!'

They had a carafe of white wine in the bottom, packed among plastic bags of ice-cubes. Luce poured it out and carefully handed the glasses around with her eyes fixed firmly on them so that they wouldn't be spilled, before she took out the tiny savouries that Faith had made and offered them around.

Teresa sighed with pleasure. 'Lovely! Tell me, Mr Ramsay, what brings you to New Zealand? Are you working on another play?'

'At the moment, no,' he returned. 'But I think I have an idea for one. I'm visiting my sister, as it happens. She and her husband own a farm around here.'

'On the coast,' Jolie informed them, then subsided as he looked at her. She was obviously attracted to him. Just as obvious was her awe.

'Will this new play be set here?' This was Faith, interested.

'Part of it, perhaps.' His eyes were a strange colour, goldy-brown around the iris merging into a wide band of clear hard green. In spite of being English he didn't wear sunglasses, so Luce had an excellent view of them when he looked at her. As he was doing now, almost as though she was some kind of scientific specimen.

That nagging feeling of familiarity fretted at her nerves, but she knew that probably she had seen his photograph in a magazine or a newspaper. He possessed the kind of features it would be hard to forget; too tough for conventional good looks but with a hard forcefulness which impinged far more readily on the senses. Once seen, never forgotten, she thought, and because the thought was ironic she smiled, then looked up from her drink to find him watching her again, the heavy lids half lowered so that all that she could see was a gleam of colour beneath them. There was nothing to be read from his expression. He seemed to have the knack of revealing only what he wished of the thoughts behind the sexy mask of his features.

Luce schooled her face into blandness, turning her head so that all he could see was the curve of her cheek and the small, rounded chin, unaware that she also displayed the long lovely line of throat and breast, the sweep of dark lashes against her pale skin.

Fortunately she wasn't needed to keep the conversation alive. Teresa and Faith managed that very successfully, both bringing their considerable assets to entertain him.

At least, Luce thought with a spice of malice, he would see that not all New Zealanders were as obvious as Jolie, who was sitting there with a sulky pouting mouth and sullen eyes, bored with Faith's amusing commentary on casting the Drama Club's latest effort.

'We thought about doing *Saturday's Harvest*,' Faith was saying now, 'but we decided against it in the end. Not enough strong women in the club.' She grinned, 'So we did *Charley's Aunt* instead.'

He chuckled, enjoying her amusement. 'Do you all act?'

'Teresa and I,' said Faith. 'Luce comes to the first night each time.'

Luce felt those eyes on her profile. When he spoke his tones were lowered, as intimate as though the other three were lifeless models.

'Not interested, Miss Laurenson?'

She had to turn, and said bluntly, 'No talent, Mr Ramsay.'

Jolie stared at her. 'But you wouldn't be able to remember anyway, would you? I mean,' looking bewildered, 'with your handicap it would be impossible, surely.'

There was an odd silence, then Luce shrugged. 'My memory for most things is excellent.'

'But you've *lost* your memory,' Jolie persisted, ignoring Faith's frown. 'How can you remember?'

Luce said gently, 'I can't remember anything of my life before two years ago, but for everything since then my memory functions perfectly.'

'Weird,' Jolie observed, shivering. 'Don't you think it's weird, Conn?'

Against her will Luce looked across at him, met the cool implacable stare with a shock of recognition which sent apprehension scudding along her nerves.

'You seemed to have adjusted very well to it,' he commented without expression.

A wry smile touched her lips, made her suddenly mature. 'There's not much else one can do. If your memory has gone, it's gone. No effort of will can bring it back.'

'Perhaps you don't want it back,' he remarked calmly, watching her.

For a minuscule part of a second every muscle in Luce's body tensed. She knew that she had gone pale, and knew that he had missed nothing of her reaction to his suggestion.

'Perhaps,' she returned lightly. 'God knows what murky secrets I have hidden away.' She set the wine down and looked across at him with an assumption of amusement which didn't fool him a bit. 'I'd make you an offer of my experience, Mr Ramsay, but I'm afraid it's too dull to make good theatre.'

'I'll be the judge of that.'

The hint of challenge in the deep tones brought her head up. He was smiling, but the smile was as watchful as his regard. Beside her Faith made an abrupt little movement, then drained the wine from her glass, saying heartily:

'Where do you get the ideas for your plays, Mr Ramsay?'

It was a clumsy attempt to break the inexplicable tension, but he followed her lead. Or rather, he allowed her to change the subject. Luce swallowed, knowing that this man was always fully in control of any conversation he took part in.

'Conn,' he said, not looking at anyone but Luce. 'I know enough about New Zealanders to know that you use first names on introduction here. As for the ideas,' he smiled, and met Faith's eyes, 'you've just seen one born. Thank you for your offer, Luce.'

She did not need Jolie's hot brown stare to convince herself that she had made a mistake. Like a fool she had challenged him, and he had taken up her unspoken gauntlet, daring her to refuse him now. Adrenalin pumped into her veins; she had to stifle an impulse to jump to her feet and run like a hare back along the sunlit beach. But she knew—who better?—that for her there was no place to go. Unconsciously her hands gripped together, then relaxed as she told herself that she had nothing to fear from him. No one could hurt her unless she allowed them to. She would not permit him to get close to her in any way.

'Better talk it over with Mattie Jameson,' Faith advised, her calm level tones easing the panic which had clutched at Luce. Conn lifted his eyebrows and she explained, 'The hospital's psychiatrist. She keeps an eye on Luce, telling her every six months that she's delightfully normal.'

'Except that she can't remember beyond the last two years.' Jolie's tones were ambiguous, but the message she hurled at Luce was only too clear. Stay away, her gaze warned. He's mine.

You can have him. For one horrified moment Luce thought she had spoken her thoughts aloud, but once more Faith had stepped into the breach and was discussing a production of *Romeo and Juliet* which had gained notoriety in London, and as Conn too had seen it they enjoyed the next several minutes tearing it to bits. He was clever, a master of understatement; he used a caustic wit, but there was no malice in his comments. Enormously sure of himself, and why not? A man like that had every reason to be confident. He had every-thing—talent, brains, the kind of personality that was a stark challenge to any woman.

After that the sun wrapped himself in a veil of high, gauzy clouds which effectively blocked out more heat than was pleasant, with the result that they decided to go home. Nothing was said during the goodbyes of any further meeting.

'You didn't like him,' Faith observed as they sped back along the Ruakaka flats towards Whangarei.

'Not particularly.'

Teresa chuckled. 'All that untrammelled masculinity is a bit much, isn't it? Do you think Jolie has any idea what she's getting into?'

'Jolie is an arrogant little half-wit,' Faith said with considerable asperity, 'and she's well due for a fall, but I feel sorry for her. Of course she doesn't know! She can't see beyond the fact that he's seething with Teresa's animal magnetism.'

'I only wish I had half of his supply,' Teresa informed her, grinning. 'But I'm rather glad that Greg isn't so well endowed. He'd have patients killing themselves for love of him!'

'Not a good idea,' Faith agreed. 'Conn Ramsay has not only got that terrific sex appeal, but he's hard and too cynical with it. Combine that with a brilliant mind and a total disregard of other people's feelings, and you've got a dangerous man. Trouble with a capital T, in fact.'

'I gather you didn't like him,' said Teresa, mild astonishment in her voice.

Faith smiled. 'Oh, I liked him, but he's no threat to me.' She flashed a quick look in the rear-vision mirror, her dark eyes thoughtful. 'How about you, Luce?'

'He's too arrogant.' Luce was exhausted, as though just being in his presence drained her. 'Jolie is welcome to him.'

'I don't think it's Jolie he's interested in,' Faith said

calmly. 'He couldn't take his eyes off you, Luce.'

'Perhaps he likes blondes,' she retorted flippantly, masking her tiredness with a smile. 'Or perhaps he wants to mine me for information and make a hit out of a case of amnesia. I wonder if I could claim half of the profits?'

They whiled away the rest of the trip home spending those mythical profits, but later that evening Faith remarked à propos of nothing, 'You'd better let Mattie Jameson check you over, Luce, in case the handsome brute does want to pick your brains.'

'Do you really think he does?' Putting down her magazine, Teresa drew her knees up on to the chair, her blue eyes sombre as they rested on the pure lines of Luce's profile. 'I thought it was a novel line, myself.'

'Possibly, but he strikes me as possessing an insatiable desire for experience. Secondhand, if he can't acquire it himself.' Faith eyed her newly-varnished nails, frowning. 'He might find Luce's looks appealing, but I'll bet he'll pump her dry while he's edging her towards the bedroom.'

A great flood of colour washed up across the fine skin. 'Do you think that's what he has in mind?' Luce asked, surprised at the violence of her own reactions. She had been propositioned before, and was well able to cope, so why the juvenile blush at the thought of Conn Ramsay's hard features flushed with desire?

'Of course he has.' Teresa laughed, folding her arms around her knees as she watched the remnants of Luce's blush fade. 'That's what they all have in mind, as you should know by now. Might be different for the handsome brute, however. I'll bet not many say no to him.'

'There's always a first time,' Luce murmured, pulling a record free from its cover. Her fingers slackened; for a moment she thought she was going to faint, but the sensation was fleeting. After a moment she put the record on to the turntable and walked back to her chair as the superb voice of Joan Sutherland filled the air.

'Are you cold?'

She shook her head at Teresa's enquiry, leaning back in the chair to listen as the magnificent pathos of the Mad Scene from *Lucia di Lammermoor* filled the room.

They were darlings, Teresa and Faith. Sometimes she thought that had it not been for their unobtrusive support over the past two years she might have gone mad. They worried over her, and Conn Ramsay's appearance and apparent interest concerned them, Faith especially. It was like having two older sisters without the hassles she believed were endemic in a family situation. Somehow she knew that in that life which lay hidden in the depths of her subconscious there had been no sisters, no brothers. So it was pleasant to have acquired two such substitutes.

Not for much longer, however, for both planned to marry in the near future. And therein lay the cause of their concern. Neither liked the thought of her fending for herself. Behind their attitudes lay the unexpressed hope that some day her memory might come back, but Luce herself had given up any expectation of that. From the first time she had wakened in that impersonal hospital ward she had known that her memory was gone for ever. There had never been a ray of light, nothing to illuminate the darkness of her past, except that occasionally she was visited by a feeling of *déjà vu*, of having been here before, such as had occurred when she saw Conn Ramsay. Because they led to nothing she had learned to discount such experiences, refusing now to strive for the memory which had proved so elusive.

In a way she was quite content. And Conn Ramsay, she vowed as the music swelled to its finale, was not going to upset that contentment. Even supposing he wanted to; he did not know their address and had made no attempt to get it, so it was more than possible that Faith was wrong and he was not interested in a slender, pale creature with no memory, certainly none of the robust sensuality that characterised Jolie.

Why should he be, when he had Jolie obviously willing to indulge him? If he wanted a holiday affair he need look no farther. For herself, Luce decided, she did not like the man, with his probing callous glance and air of watchfulness.

Unfortunately for her peace of mind he turned up at the shop at close to twelve the very next day, walking in through the door with an air of owning the whole universe and not thinking much of his possession. Those green eyes roved the shop, finally settling where Luce stood, cool and remote, removing a ring from the locked case so that a woman could try it on.

'I love rubies,' the customer gushed now, trying to force it over her knuckle. 'I could have it made bigger, of course.'

'Of course,' Luce agreed tonelessly, inwardly rebelling at the thought. The ring was a dainty setting of tiny rubies and diamonds which needed a long slender finger to set it off.

Apparently the customer agreed, for she frowned. 'Although it's not what I had in mind, really. Too—too bitsy. I'll leave it, thank you.'

All through the inane conversation Luce was aware of his stare, hating the delicate colour it brought across her cheekbones. Now she turned to him armed with the few moments' warning of his presence.

'What can I show you?' she asked.

He smiled, but the eyes remained as cool as green glass. 'What a prim little voice! Hadn't you better lock that away?'

As he spoke he lifted the ring, then, so swiftly that she was completely taken aback, thrust it on to her finger, holding it there with a cruel grip when she tried to pull away.

'What are you doing——?' She tried to ball her fingers into a fist, but he held them extended, hurting her so that she gasped and went white.

'Leave me alone,' she whispered in a shocked voice,

lifting a hand to her temple.

'Does your head hurt?'

'I don't—no, no, it doesn't.' It was no use trying to fight him, so she let her hand lie resistlessly in his, trembling with reaction and a kind of fear she had never before experienced.

'Lesson one,' he said, smiling yet meaning every word of it. 'Don't fight me, Luce. I've made a habit of winning and I don't intend to stop now.'

It was a threat in spite of the smile, but he let her hand go. She turned away, fumbling with the key to the cabinet, terrified that he would come and open it himself.

He waited, however, until she had replaced the lovely thing, and then said as if the strange little incident had never happened: 'I want something for my sister. It's her birthday next week.'

'What did you have in mind?' The often repeated words steadied her, gave her back her confidence.

A smile which mocked her manner twisted the hard mouth. 'Her husband buys her jewellery, but she collects porcelain and glass. You know her tastes.'

'I do?' She was astonished, prepared to bet that none of the customers bore any resemblance to the man before her.

'Yes,' he said, with that smile which was not a smile. 'She's Sonia McLeod.'

'Oh!'

He laughed, the fierce features softening into humour. 'You may well look astonished.'

Indeed she had every reason. Sonia McLeod was a small woman, a dainty elegant little creature with no hint of her brother's strong features except, perhaps . . . yes, the eyes were the same. Golden-brown around the iris, then the wide band of green enclosed by a black edging. Startling eyes, but while they made Conn resemble a bird of prey they gave his sister a very clear, piercing regard without the cruelty.

Sonia McLeod was a charmer, her brother was a danger and the sooner she got rid of him the better. Fortunately there was a piece which should appeal to her.

'We have a Lalique vase,' she said, taking him back to the locked cabinet. 'It's not an antique, but it is beautiful.' It was also expensive, but she had no idea how much he wanted to spend on his sister.

Carefully she removed the vase, her fingers white against the electric blue glass.

'Very pretty,' he observed drily. 'I'll take it.'

He didn't even blink at the price, which was high enough to have convinced Luce that the piece was doomed to remain in the shop for a long time.

And for a man who seemed to suffer from a barely suppressed impatience, he waited calmly enough while she carefully packed the lovely delicate thing, watching her absorbed intentness with an impassive expression.

'Do you want it gift-wrapped?' she asked when she had packed it to her satisfaction.

'Of course.'

The note of irony in the crisp voice brought a trace of colour to her cheeks, but she ignored it, wrapping the box in the gaily patterned paper with deft fingers.

'There,' she said, holding it out to him. 'I hope she likes it.'

'I'm sure she will.'

Meaningless words, so why did they rasp over a dry throat and why did she avoid his eyes as if she possessed a guilty secret?

It was a relief when the owner, Graeme Hunter, appeared from the back of the shop, saying, 'Lunchtime, isn't it, Luce?'

He was waiting for her when she came through from the cloakroom, the parcel tucked casually under his arm as he frowned at a particularly fine Spanish sword. Evidently he had frightened Graeme off, for he was in the depths of the display case busily rearranging the jewellery. Conn walked beside her without saying anything until they reached the street, when he observed:

'Trusting soul, isn't he?'

Luce shrugged, angry at his casual attitude. 'You must look trustworthy, I suppose. Graeme is no fool.'

'Do you think I look trustworthy?'

'No,' she said coldly. 'I think you look dangerous.'

Dark brows lifted in mocking amusement. 'You don't believe in hiding behind platitudes, do you? Why should I look dangerous?'

'I'm sure you're not interested in my opinion of you.' They had come to the corner of the road and she said swiftly, 'I have to go down here. Goodbye, Mr Ramsay. Enjoy the rest of your holiday.'

'Not so fast!' Incredibly he caught her wrist, preventing her from leaving. 'Have lunch with me.'

His grip didn't hurt, but beneath his fingers Luce's skin prickled as if his touch was poisonous. 'Let me go,' she said very quietly, her face set in lines of astonishment and anger.

'When you agree to have lunch with me.' He wasn't in the least intimidated by her anger or the cold scorn in her glance.

'No.'

'Why not?'

People were beginning to eye them now, some with sly interest, some with open curiosity and several with broad grins. They must look like lovers quarrelling, she thought, and what colour she possessed drained away leaving her as white as a marble statue.

'I don't want to,' she told him thinly.

'I wonder who has the stronger will?' As her gaze widened he smiled with narrow emphasis. 'Because I want you to, very much.'

For some reason she could not sustain her glare. Beneath the mockery in his expression there was laughter as if he invited her to share a joke. Her eyes fell to rest on the lean strength of his fingers.

Perhaps he saw her weakening, for he lifted her hand and kissed the delicate veins at her wrist, saying against the skin, 'Please, Luce. I promise to behave.'

Later she told herself that she should have stood firm and refused him, but an instinct told her that he would have found some way to break down her resistance. As it was the heat of his mouth on her skin made her jerk away as if he had branded her.

Half beneath her breath she asked, 'Why don't you ask Jolie? Affairs are not my line.'

'And they are hers?' He was smiling as he led her across the road. Several girls looked him over, their appreciation obvious, but he didn't appear to see them. When she said nothing he resumed, 'You haven't a very high opinion of her.'

'I hardly know her.'

'But what you know you dislike? I wonder why? Because you see her as a threat?'

'Oh, for heaven's sake!' She stopped, very nearly tripping up a large woman with a shopping bag who glowered indignantly at her. 'What is this? It's none of your business how I feel about Jolie Stewart—or anyone else. Do you think that just because you write plays you have a right to probe into other people's minds? Not mine, Mr Ramsay. What there is of it is a very private place.'

'You're obstructing the footpath.' He smiled with irony yet a certain sympathy as she jerked her arm from his grip.

It occurred to her that he would be a man whom it was almost impossible to fool. A further even less palatable thought struck her. It was probably this intuitive understanding that made him so clever a playwright, and so great a cynic.

Perhaps he understood why she found herself sitting opposite him in a small restaurant she knew only by hearsay because it was too expensive for most of her escorts. Trust him to have discovered it and to be perfectly at home.

'I'm not hungry,' she said tonelessly, eyeing the menu with a complete lack of interest.

'You don't look as though you eat enough.' Ignoring her protests, he ordered for them both, then asked with calm impertinence, 'How old are you, Luce?'

'Twenty.' Her lashes, thick and blatantly dark, swept down to cover the cool depths of her eyes.

'So you were eighteen when you lost your memory.'

She shrugged. 'Obviously.'

'Does it make you feel uncomfortable to talk about it?'

'No, not really.' Waiting until the wine waiter had gone, she said huskily, 'It's like a dream, now. Apparently I fell downstairs—I was reading, which was a stupid thing to do—and I hit my head. When I woke up—blankness.'

'Did you remember your name?'

She sipped the wine, enjoying the dry, crisp taste on her tongue. 'No, but when they told it to me—it—it sounded familiar.'

'What else did you remember?'

'About myself, nothing.' It was probably part of his stock-in-trade, but he was easy to talk to. It couldn't be the wine, she had barely tasted it. Almost imperceptibly she relaxed, staring into the pale depths of the wine glass. 'But I remember—or at least, I can retrieve—all of the information I must have learned at school. I know the plots of books that I've read, I know music, I can recall films.'

'But you've lost the events of your life.'

Luce nodded. 'Just that.'

'Is it likely that you'll regain your memory now?'

A shiver feathered across her skin, making her suddenly clammy. 'No. Apparently if I'd been going to it would have happened by now. Oh, the doctor has never said so, but I can see that she doesn't hold out much hope.'

'You don't seem to care,' he observed speculatively, his glance shadowed yet intent on her face.

Again that shrug. 'I don't. I'm happy.'

'Meaning that you weren't before?'

The words hung, sharp and hurtful on the air. Luce drew a painful breath as her fingers tightened on the stem of her glass. 'I don't know,' she murmured, lifting tormented eyes to meet the cold penetration of his.

After a moment he said almost gently, 'It's strange that no one claimed you. Surely the police must have advertised—or appealed, or *something*,'

'I don't know.' She swallowed, saw his eyes linger on the pale length of her throat and felt a prickle of heat crawl along her skin. There was sensual appreciation in his regard and a challenge; the arrival of the waiter was a relief.

The food was delicious. To her surprise she discovered that she was hungry, after all, so she made a good meal, helped by the fact that during it they spoke of uncontroversial subjects.

'Better than a carton of yoghurt and an apple, wasn't it?'

She smiled. 'An orange, as it happened. To be exact a tangelo. But yes, thank you, it was. Doesn't your sister mind if you desert her during the day?'

'Sonia knows me too well to be surprised at anything I do,' he told her drily, stirring the black depths of his coffee. He looked up and held her eyes, smoothly sure of himself, and smiled. 'She's an extremely busy woman, with a house and a farm and a husband as well as two children to keep tabs on. Besides,' with a return to cynicism, 'she knows I'm buying her birthday present.'

'It seems strange to think of you with a sister,' she remarked idly.

There was a hint of a silence before he retorted, 'And how does a man with a sister differ from the norm?'

'I don't know,' she said, bewildered by her remark and his astringent reply. 'It was a stupid thing to say.

You seem—I suppose it's because you seem so self-sufficient.'

'My upbringing was enough to produce an excess of self-sufficiency. My parents believed that boarding school was the answer to all disciplinary problems—and to be fair, there were a lot. I was a swine of a child. So I was sent away at a remarkably early age even for England, and from then on we saw each other only in the holidays. It doesn't make for close, enduring family ties.'

The caustic note in his voice warned her from any further probing. 'I suppose not,' she said, feeling profoundly sorry for him. 'Did your sister go away to school, too?'

'Oh yes. My parents followed the traditional pattern. They almost bankrupted themselves to give us a good education. Sonia was expected to marry well, but unfortunately she disappointed them by falling in love with a raw Colonial.' He saw her eyes widen and gave a slow sardonic smile. 'Yes, they really thought that way. Further disappointments lay in store, however. I had no desire to become a banker or stockbroker. My writing they never considered. When I left school and began wasting time they washed their hands of me entirely.'

'You sound bitter.'

He nodded. 'I was, for a long time. Then, after a space of ten years or so, I went back.'

'And . . .'

'And they were two old, tired people, caught in a straitjacket not of their own making. Not unfeeling, just unimaginative. It was a very salutary lesson. Before that I'd paid lip service to the notion that there are two sides to every question; after that I knew it was true.'

Strangely, this made Luce look up, startled. For a moment she stared at him as if it was the very first time she had seen him, her gaze wide, almost unfocussed as she took in the hard excitement of his features. Her breath caught in her throat. She expelled it with a sigh and set her coffee cup down.

'So all's well that ends well,' she said flatly. 'I'll have to go—it's almost time for me to be back.'

Conn looked at her with the watchful intensity she so disliked but made no attempt to stop her. When they arrived back at the shop he seemed unsurprised at her haste to get away from him.

She was unmannerly in her eagerness to say goodbye. An ironic smile curled his mouth.

'I'll see you around,' he said softly.

Doubt darkened her glance, but she merely nodded and thanked him for the meal before diving hurriedly inside.

CHAPTER TWO

MATTIE JAMESON had kept an eye on Luce ever since she had been brought unconscious to the hospital. She was middle-aged and thin, and like all of her profession it was difficult to pin her down to a definite statement about anything, but especially where Luce was concerned. .

Now she looked across her desk at the girl, her wise eyes sympathetic. 'You know I can't answer that, Luce. I have no idea whether or not your memory is likely to come back. We're dealing with the mind, and there are immense areas about which we know nothing. Why the sudden interest?'

'Something somebody said.' Luce's every instinct was to avoid mention of Conn Ramsay, but she told her, adding ruefully, 'He seems to think that I might be an interesting subject for study. Faith insisted I see you first.'

'Did she now?' Mattie's fingers smoothed lovingly over the petals of one of a cluster of pinks in the vase on her desk. 'Amnesia is a form of hysteria, a defence mechanism, if you like. Normally it wears off after a few days or weeks. Occasionally, as in your case, it lasts. But there is *always* the possibility of your memory returning. Usually it needs some stimulus, some nudging in the right direction. That was why we tried to discover your background and where you'd come from. If you remember, you weren't very enthusiastic.'

Luce nodded, her hair given a pale radiance by the warm eager light of the sun. 'Yes, I remember. It was odd, but I felt so tired, I just wanted to sleep.'

'Have you done anything about it since then?'

'No,' she answered, sounding surprised. 'I—well,

27

when the police said that they couldn't find out anything about me I just left it.'

'Hasn't it ever occurred to you that such a reaction was—well—unusual?'

The tip of Luce's tongue wet her lips. The spicy scent of pinks was suddenly heavy on the air. 'I suppose it is,' she said huskily. 'But I was never posted as missing, was I? I must have been alone in the world, because there was no one looking for me.'

'No one appeared to be interested,' Mattie agreed. 'You sound English, but there was nobody of your name who'd come into the country in the last few months before your accident, so we concluded you'd been here some time. We drew a complete blank everywhere we went. Almost as if you'd covered your tracks.'

'Like a criminal!'

The psychiatrist smiled. 'Relax—the police did their best, and there was nothing to show that you'd been mixed up in anything unlawful. But I've always felt that for some reason you wanted no one to know where you were. And that reason is why your mind blanked out the personal part of your life—why it still blanks it out. The answer lies in the past.'

'And my mind won't let me go there because of what I might find.'

'Exactly.' Then Mattie added with her usual caution, 'At least, I think so.'

There was silence while Luce thought this over, her forehead crinkling at the implications. 'Do you think I should talk things over with Mr Ramsay?' she asked nervously.

'Luce, I can't give you advice. I think you're now strong enough to take whatever you uncover without cracking up. It may not be pleasant, but you have strength and courage. Perhaps you needed the rest that amnesia gives. If you want to remember now you must convince your subconscious that the knowledge can no longer harm you.'

'You think I should try.'

But the older woman shook her head. 'No, the decision must be yours alone. So far you've drifted along; now this man has caused you to think seriously, and that's a good thing. What's he like?'

'Forceful,' Luce told her wryly. 'You know, the sort of man you read about but don't believe in. Tough, but clever—too clever.'

'You seem to have learnt a lot about him for such a short acquaintance.'

Luce was very still. 'Yes, it's odd, isn't it? But he—oh, he makes himself felt.'

'Some people have it,' Mattie murmured. 'Character—charisma—whatever. It's an interesting field. I seem to remember that he has more than his share of looks.'

'Oh, he's an impressive creature.' It took an effort for Luce to keep her voice light, untouched by emotion. 'Like a hawk, all angles and planes, no curves. Even his chin is square. And green eyes, opaque like jade. You can't look into them and see what he's thinking.' A shiver touched her skin, fretting at her nerves as Conn's brooding hard features sprang to her recollection. With a smile she finished, 'Not your average likeable man at all! He looks as though he knows hell like his own backyard.'

Which was a strange thing to say. Mattie never showed surprise, but at this she enquired rather anxiously, 'You sound as though you dislike him, my dear.'

'I don't think anyone dislikes Mr Ramsay. He's the sort you hate.'

'Or love.'

The pale hair belled out as Luce shook her head. She smiled to cover a dark foreboding which held her in thrall. 'No. Isn't it true that love can only be love if it's reciprocated? Conn Ramsay has never loved in his life, I'm certain. He has the power of fascination, but not to evoke love.'

'A very sensual man.'

'Oh, he's that.' But Luce had tired of the subject, or perhaps she was afraid of revealing more of the turmoil that the thought of Conn evoked. Smiling, she looked across the desk, met Mattie's shrewd, compassionate eyes with laughter in the cloud-coloured depths of her own. 'Who knows, my experiences might be immortalised in a work by Ramsay. Heady thoughts for a nobody!'

'My dear girl, you'll never be a nobody, even if your memory refuses ever to come back.' Mattie looked down at the flower in her hands, frowning at its perfection. 'But I would think very carefully before you encouraged him. Forgive me, but you don't strike me as being particularly experienced, and if my memory for gossip is at all accurate Conn Ramsay is not the sort of man I would like my daughter to cut her teeth on.'

'Oh, I shan't fall for him.' Luce's voice was very soft, but the determination in it rang louder than any bell. 'I think if I remember anything it's that I'm a survivor. Anyone who gets involved with him just has to be a loser! Besides,' she added calmly, 'he may change his mind.'

However, she was not surprised to come out from the shop at five-thirty a few days later and find him waiting for her. Leaning against a car, he was tall and disturbing in jeans and a thin fine sweater which emphasised the width and power of his shoulders. When he saw her he straightened up and came towards her, an ambiguous smile not softening his mouth at all. A woman walking towards them looked greedily at him, her expression openly envious, then flushed when she saw Luce's swift glance. He had not seen that quick calculating scrutiny, for he watched Luce as she came towards him without sparing a glance anywhere else.

'Hello,' she said uncertainly, feeling that merciless regard pinned her for inspection.

'Hello.' He spoke softly. 'Come to dinner with me.'

Just momentarily her teeth clenched on to her bottom lip. 'You don't give much warning, do you.'

'Yes or no, make up your mind.'

His withdrawal into boredom angered her. What the devil did he think he was up to, treating her as if she should be grateful that he had thought of asking her out! A muscle jerked against her jawbone, tightening it.

'No, thank you.'

'Aha,' he mocked, the green eyes narrowing. 'So there are tiny claws beneath that touch-me-not veneer. Get in and I'll drive you home.'

Luce hesitated, but only momentarily. However equivocal his attitude it was stupid to turn down a lift home.

But she should have taken that purposeful jaw into consideration, for almost immediately it become apparent that he had no intention of taking her home.

'Is this an abduction?' she enquired icily.

He smiled. 'Yes. It's Sonia's birthday; she wants you to come out for dinner.'

'Why didn't you say?' Luce twisted angrily against the confining band of the seat-belt. 'Honestly, you're the most infuriating man I've ever met! I can't go out in my working clothes.'

'I would have taken you home to change.'

'Take me home now.'

'No.' He smiled again, his profile hard against the pale sky.

'Oh—you're maddening!'

'Second lesson,' he said mockingly. 'I'm quite unscrupulous when it comes to getting my own way.'

'Why qualify it? Why not say totally unscrupulous?' she demanded sarcastically, her voice as sweet as honey.

Conn laughed at that, apparently finding her entertaining, although it was hard to tell whether his amusement was genuine or not. Without checking the progress of the car he lifted one of her hands from her lap and held it to his mouth. She felt the tip of his tongue against the palm and was submerged by a wave of sensation terrifying in its strength.

Jerking her hand away, she turned her head so that he could not see how his touch had affected her. Beneath the blue linen of her jacket her breasts rose and fell with the intensity of her emotion; after a moment she relaxed enough to see that they had left the main road north and were heading east towards the coast. The countryside was very smooth and lush-looking, many deciduous trees lightening the landscape with their new leaves, the grass green and thick beneath the warm sky. The pastures were in superb condition.

'My brother-in-law is a farmer,' Conn informed her blandly. 'Sheep and cattle.'

'How did he and your sister meet?'

'She was here on a working holiday. I've never enquired, but from what Sonia has let drop I gather that they loathed each other at first sight and had an unusually tempestuous courtship, finally ending, to everyone's surprise including Sonia's, with wedding bells.'

It seemed easier to follow his lead, so she said, 'Your sister doesn't look in the least tempestuous!'

'Looks can be deceiving. She might resemble a wax doll, but she can whip up a storm when she wants to. She needs a firm hand, and they don't come much firmer than Ryan.'

A faint frown marred the smoothness of her forehead. 'He sounds a bit ominous.'

'Let's just say that if I were ever in trouble. I can think of no one else I'd rather go to.' But it was obvious that he could not imagine such a situation. Neither could Luce. He was altogether too much in command to ever need help.

Ryan McLeod was every bit as tough as his brother-in-law. Indeed, in some ways they were startlingly alike, for both possessed that immense self-assurance which comes from a cold, clear recognition of one's faults and strengths.

Two overpowering creatures, Luce thought, as she shook hands with him. He was pleasant, but the dark eyes were cool, only warming when they rested on his wife.

Sonia smiled. 'They do tend to swamp any bystanders, don't they,' she said with amused understanding. 'Come into the drawing room. I've lit a fire even though it's a warm evening.'

Chatting easily, she led the way into an enormous room, superbly furnished in a mixture of antique and the best of modern furniture. It suited its owners so perfectly that Luce was not in the least surprised to learn that McLeods had lived here for generations. Sonia had married into the landed gentry, she thought frivolously.

It was a pleasant evening, although there were undercurrents. Sonia could not have been more charming, but her husband, in spite of his superb manners, kept his thoughts very much to himself. Luce was nervous, made uneasy by the way Conn watched her from beneath his lashes even when he spoke to his sister or her husband.

It gave her that cold creepiness between the shoulder blades which can attack the bravest person when they are being spied upon or stalked.

She would not give way to it. With the faintest lift of her chin she set herself out to respond to her hostess's overtures. To any outside observer it would have appeared a very successful little dinner party, for there was much laughter, not a little wit and plenty of good conversation. Luce enjoyed herself in spite of the prickle of tension through her nerves. Such was the McLeods' courtesy that she didn't know whether or not they had been warned of her amnesia.

Until Sonia said, sighing, 'I'll never get accustomed to spring here. I like my spring to arrive with a bang and trumpet voluntaries, blue skies and daffodils after the miseries of winter. Here we have jonquils before winter has got under way, the lambs and calves arrive

in July, which is in the depths, and it's only the oak
trees which unfurl their leaves in spring. Don't you
prefer the English spring, Luce?'

'I don't remember,' Luce answered quietly, smiling
because so often amnesia made people embarrassed.
'But spring here is lovely. The days seem suddenly to
get longer and the tea-tree blooms all along the road-
sides like a late fall of snow, and the air is soft and rich.
I love it.'

'Luce isn't in the least worried by her lack of
memories,' Conn observed smoothly, his expression
enigmatic.

Sonia shivered. 'I don't think I could be so calm about
it. How about you, Ryan?'

'It depends entirely on the memories.'

Which led to a spirited discussion about a story of
Dickens on just that subject, and from there the conversation ranged far and wide in the world of literature.
Luce knew that she surprised them by her familiarity
with the works they mentioned; it was a normal reaction
and after a while they accepted her knowledge.

But she was glad when the evening was over. It had
been exhausting. For the first time she realised how
much she moved among people who were in some way
connected with the hospital and who accepted her condition without comment. It made life much easier for
her.

'Now, you must come and see us again,' Sonia pressed
her as they left.

'Thank you.' But Luce was noncommittal. She liked
Sonia very much; it was the two men in her life who
were frightening.

As if she had spoken her thoughts Conn said softly,
'Ryan likes you. Which leaves only me.'

'I—I don't know what you mean.'

'No?' He let the silence develop into tension before
continuing, 'You like Sonia, that was obvious. And
Ryan is no threat to you, so that means that it's me that

you distrust. That's why you brushed off her invitation, wasn't it?'

'Was it that obvious?'

'Worried?'

Luce sighed, sinking back into the seat. 'I don't like being rude, and she was so kind.'

'She's a kindly soul,' he agreed without patronage. 'One of the few really kind people I know. No, she won't be upset. You intrigue her, just as you intrigue me.'

The skin tightened over her cheekbones, but she managed to infuse a note of amusement into her voice when she spoke. 'Professionally, I hope.'

'Why? Do I frighten you?'

'I may have lost my memory, but I still have instincts,' she said drily, 'and every instinct I possess is warning me that you're dangerous.'

He chuckled. 'So you've told me before. Elucidate.'

'You know darned well what I mean! I don't have to spell it out. You're as tough as whip leather and every edge is a cutting one. You hurt people.'

'I can't approve of that appalling mixed metaphor—leather has no cutting edges. And you must have packed a lot of experience into your pre-amnesiac life to be able to recognise my type so swiftly.'

The derision in his voice hurt, as it had been meant to, stripping away confidence so that she found herself wondering dismally how on earth she could think of him being interested enough in her to be a menace. She swallowed, feeling sick and stupid.

A wave of sensation swamped her with its fierce intimation that she had been here before, that a long time ago this man had used just that note of ridicule when he spoke to her.

Unknown to herself she must have moaned, for he demanded roughly, 'What's the matter? Are you ill?'

The car stopped. Without bothering to dip the lights he turned to her, switching the interior light on so that he could see her pinched features, the haunted grey eyes enormous in her white face.

'Luce?' he asked softly, touching her forehead. He grimaced as he felt the beads of sweat there, but the dark eyes held her pinned. 'What is it?'

Already the weakness was passing, but she asked hoarsely, 'Do I know you?'

Nothing changed, not one muscle in the dark good-looking face moved, yet she felt his withdrawal as clearly as if he had flung her from him and the pain made her close her eyes.

'No,' Conn said at last. 'No, you know nothing of me, Luce. Nothing at all. Why?'

Deep breathing had always helped. Now, with eyes still closed, she initiated the rhythm. Slowly the fear and the pain receded, taking with it that hint of recollection.

After several minutes she said, 'I'm sorry that happened. It always frightens me when it does.'

'Why?' He set the car in motion again. 'Surely you should be pleased at the thought of regaining your memory.'

Carefully she wiped her face with her handkerchief then dried the cold dampness of her palms. 'No. It's as though if I dared to remember I'd find myself in a hell that I can't escape.' She paused before finishing in stifled tones, 'It's like living on a ledge. A clear sunlit ledge, safe and snug and pretty, with people who are kind. If I miss my footing I'll fall off the ledge into the abyss.'

'Are you so sure that what lies buried in your sub-conscious is unpleasant? You could have lived a per-fectly ordinary life, with a family and friends and lovers, and the amnesia could be the result of the fall.'

The moon had risen while they dined and was riding high in the sky, its light dimming all but the brightest stars. Beneath the deceptive glamour of its radiance the countryside lay revealed, a mysterious, heartcatching fairyland. The headlights picked up the double green gleam of a small animal's eyes; a few seconds later Conn swerved to miss a hedgehog snuffling its busy, dangerous way across the road.

Such beauty caught Luce by the throat. Huskily she said, 'You're probably quite right. But apparently none of those family, friends or lovers cared enough to want to know where I was.'

'And that hurts.'

'Oddly enough, it does.'

'That means,' Conn said without emphasis, 'there must be someone, somewhere; someone you hoped would come after you.'

Again she was surprised at how easy it was to talk to him—and how astute he was. The sensation was unpleasant. By revealing so much of her mind to him she felt that she was exposing herself to a danger she could not yet discern.

Stiffly she replied, 'Possibly. But apparently I covered my tracks so well that not even the police could trace me, so I must have been in two minds about this hypothetical someone.'

'Just as you're in two minds about me.' His smile was a swift challenging flash in the darkness. 'You don't trust me, yet you talk to me. Why?'

'I suppose . . .' she paused, marshalling her thoughts before resuming, 'I suppose it's because you offer me no sympathy. You—you don't treat me like a freak, or a halfwit. You stimulate me into thinking. And there's nothing personal in your interest.'

He laughed at that, and drove the car off the road beneath a huge oak. Before Luce had time to think he unclipped his seatbelt and turned, his hands holding her wrists together as the lock on her belt clicked free.

'How very naïve you are, my dear,' he taunted softly as he pulled her into his arms. 'Or did you think I needed encouragement?'

The steering wheel hurt her shoulder, but it was nothing compared to the pain in her heart. Those instincts she had talked of warred within her, self-preservation urging her to hit out at him while a deeper,

even more basic one told her to lie still in the hard circle
of his arm. His hand came up to her throat. He looked
down to where his finger rested against the pulse that
his touch made leap beneath the silken skin.

If he kissed her she would be sacrificed, flayed, left
naked to his gaze.

His stillness warned her that he was waiting for her to
resist. She could feel the tension in his muscles and knew
that some deep primeval hunger in him would give him
pleasure in subduing any struggles. Against the silver
sky his profile was predatory, cruel as a conqueror's
when he sees an enemy preparing for a battle in which
defeat is inevitable.

Very slowly she asked, 'Is that what you think I've
been doing? Provoking you? You give me credit for
more subtlety than I possess. I don't even like you.'

'Ah, but we know this has nothing to do with liking,'
he said, lifting his glance to rest on her mouth. 'Nothing
to do with liking, or loving. And if you don't know it,
Luce, it's time you learned.'

The throbbing pulse in her throat seemed to fascinate
him, for he touched it with his lips, smiling when it
betrayed her once more. His breath was warm against
her skin, incredibly erotic. She could smell the faint male
scent of him, feel the slight roughness of his skin when
his mouth traced a line towards the lobe of her ear.
Deep within her a fire began to burn, barely discernible
except for a strange lethargy which held her motionless
while his mouth ravished her senses.

'I can't bear this,' she moaned, turning her head away
from him.

'It gets easier as time passes.' His tongue explored the
vulnerable hollow beneath her ear, then his teeth met
on the lobe and she gasped, and put her hand out in a
blind appeal.

'Conn—please,' she whispered.

She had been kissed before, of course she had, and
usually found it enjoyable, even slightly stirring, but

there could have been nothing ever to compare with the complete abandonment to her physical self which occurred when his mouth covered hers, blotting out the plea on her lips.

Needs she had never known existed fired her to a purpose so that she moved against him convulsively, twisting to bring her body in even closer contact with the hard strength of his. She wanted—oh, God, she *wanted*! Desire held her in its terrifying, ecstatic grip; every sense fed her hunger so that she drowned in the scent and feel and taste of him. Only her eyes remained tightly closed, a kind of barrier between her brain and the full realisation of what he was doing to her.

When Conn lifted his head she reached up her hand to pull him back while sharp rigours of unsatisfied passion shook her body.

'Not here, Luce,' he muttered, his voice strangely unlike his normal incisive tones. 'A car isn't my favourite place for making love.'

Slowly she lifted her lashes, her breath coming in short gasps between her lips. He was looking at her with a strange, shuttered sensuality, his expression too controlled to be natural after such an explosion of desire.

'What is it?' she breathed.

'Nothing.' He tightened his grip but it was only to bring her upright. Once she was back in her seat he asked ironically, 'Is that your usual reaction to a kiss?'

It was like being thrown into iced water. 'No,' she answered, beyond lying. 'Is that how you kiss a woman for the first time?'

'It depends entirely on the woman.' There was a thread of mockery in his voice as he brought the seatbelt across her breast and clicked it into place. 'As we're being so frank, however, I'll admit that physically we seem to mesh.'

Which fell so far short of how she had felt that in spite of the turbulence within a faint smile touched her lips.

'No comment beyond the Mona Lisa look?'

She shook her head. 'I can't seem to think of anything to say.'

'Then I'll take you home.'

It wasn't until they had almost reached the flat that Luce realised that during the entire evening she had given no thought to letting Teresa or Faith know where she was. When she was with Conn he seemed to swamp her with his personality so that even the consideration she had thought to be an inbuilt part of her character went by the board.

He came to the door but made no attempt to touch her. She was horrified to discover that disappointment was the strongest emotion she felt, and this forced a return to the stiff manner she had first adopted.

'It's too late to try to freeze me out,' he told her with dry amusement. 'I know too much about you now.'

Silhouetted against the brightness of the moonlit garden his face was in darkness so that she could not see anything beyond the dark profile, but the sardonic note in his voice was plain. It made her shiver.

'Get inside, you're cold.'

'No,' she whispered. 'A goose walked over my grave.'

She stared up, trying to distinguish his features, unaware that her own were set in an expression of unconscious yearning.

'I'm not going to kiss you again,' he taunted. 'I've had enough excitement for one night. Goodnight, Luce.'

Presumably she said something suitable, for he laughed softly and pushed her through the open door.

Oddly enough she slept as soon as her head hit the pillow, slept long and dreamlessly so that it took Teresa a minute or two to shake her awake the next morning.

'Come *on*!' she ordered, yanking back the curtains with a ruthless hand. 'It's a beautiful day and it's ten minutes past the time you should have got up at—if you know what I mean!'

Luce groaned, but sat up. 'Oh, *lord*! What time is it?'

'Ten past seven. Coffee's made and the bathroom is free. And where did you go last night?'

It was an effort to summon up a smile, but Luce managed it, although she made sure that her back was to the older girl when she told her.

'*Really*?' Teresa was vastly intrigued. 'I told you that he was interested. Hurry up and you can tell us over breakfast.'

Which Luce did, giving a suitably expurgated description as well as apologising for not letting them know where she had been. Faith was on afternoon duty, so she had not been home when Luce failed to appear, but Teresa had been just a tiny bit worried, so she said.

'Not that I should have been,' she decided cheerfully, 'because nobody could be less likely to kick over the traces than you.'

Remembering those moments spent in Conn's arms Luce had the grace to blush slightly. If Teresa knew how ironic her statement was she would probably be appalled.

'I saw him yesterday,' Faith commented.

'Where?' Luce could have kicked herself for enquiring so eagerly, especially when she felt the heat of that tell-tale flush across her cheeks again.

'At the hospital. He was strolling around the grounds as though he owned the place.' A pause, and then she went on, 'I saw him coming out of Block Seven a little later.'

Teresa opened her mouth, thought better of what she had been going to say and closed it firmly.

'That's Mattie Jameson's block,' Luce was suddenly hollow in the stomach. 'I wonder if he tried to pump her. What a nerve!'

'Oh, he's got all the confidence in the world, that one,' Faith agreed. 'But even super colossal audacity wouldn't get Dr Jameson to talk if she didn't want to. And that's assuming that he got to see her. She can be very elusive when necessary.'

'So don't be too angry with him,' Teresa ordered, setting her coffee mug down. 'You know, if he took you to his sister's place he just might be serious.'

Luce shrugged. 'Hardly. I know her from the shop.'

'You're moving in exalted circles.' Faith was only half teasing. 'The McLeods were here very early in the piece. Ryan was quite the most desirable bachelor around before his wife came on to the scene. What did you think of them?'

Again Luce shrugged. 'Very pleasant. She's a darling, he's not the sort of person you get to know in one easy lesson. Still, I suppose she's used to dealing with complex types; no one could call Conn easy to understand either.'

The cheerful voice of the radio announcer giving the time brought instant action, but even as she walked briskly down the footpath Luce couldn't help feeling the niggling fear which Faith's disclosure had caused. The fact that it was fear that she felt, and not the anger Teresa assumed it to be, bewildered her, quite spoiling a walk that she usually enjoyed.

After a few hundred metres she determined to put Conn out of her mind, and by dint of concentrating fiercely on the gardens all decked out in spring flowers, she managed it. The sight of one particularly lovely clump of cottage pinks even brought a smile to her face, and for the rest of the day she was kept so busy that there were long periods of time when she scarcely thought of him at all.

Until Jolie Stewart walked in, superb in a black and white striped dolman dress which did wonders for her auburn hair and large brown eyes. She was just slightly too curvy, Luce thought wearily; in ten years' time she would probably be on a permanent diet, but at the moment she looked like the stuff of every young man's fantasies.

Astoundingly she gave Luce a smile which almost

fooled her into thinking that the other girl had had a change of attitude where shop assistants were concerned.

'I want to look at some jewellery,' she said, quite pleasantly. 'Especially those emerald earrings.'

They looked stunning with her colouring, the green stones opulent against the creamy skin and vivid hair. Luce said so.

'Yes, they do, don't they?' She smiled at her reflection. 'It's my birthday soon. My twenty-first. I know it doesn't mean much nowadays, but the parents are rather old-fashioned and they like to make a thing of it, so there's to be an enormous party. I think I might just work out a tactful way to mention these.'

Luce made a noncommittal noise, thinking drily that the Stewarts must be extremely wealthy if they could afford the earrings as well as a party.

Again Jolie smiled. 'Conn tells me he took you to dinner at the McLeods' last night. I'm so glad you could go; I felt a real heel letting him down at the last minute, but Mum really was sick and I just couldn't go. Dad's no use when she's not well.'

'I'm sorry to hear about it. Is she better?'

Perhaps Jolie had been expecting some sharper reaction, for beneath the offhanded note in her voice there seemed to be chagrin when she replied, 'Oh yes, just a bout of change-of-season tummy bug. I hope you enjoyed yourself.'

The avid curiosity in her brown eyes sickened Luce. As she put the earrings back in the cabinet she replied woodenly, 'Very much, thank you.'

'The McLeods are super people, aren't they? Sonia is a sweetie and Ryan——' Jolie rolled her eyes heavenwards, 'well, he still gives me goosebumps when he smiles.' She paused, expecting an answer, and when Luce said nothing resumed chattily, 'I tease Sonia by telling her that the two men in her life are the two most exciting men in New Zealand. I believe Ryan's reputation with women used to be absolutely appalling, and according to gossip columnists Conn is no better. Of course, it's different when people are friends. I mean, it's only a certain sort of girl that would—well, you know what I mean.'

Luce knew perfectly well what she meant, knew too, exactly what she was implying. And decided that if she ever heard Jolie say, 'Of course,' again in that patronising voice she would take great pleasure in kicking her.

However, she merely smiled and nodded, aware of that red-brown gaze fixed on her face, and went on locking the cabinet.

'Well, I must be off.' Yes, she was definitely disappointed. She must have hoped for some stronger reaction. 'See you around.'

Not if I can help it. Luce almost said it aloud. Indeed, for a moment she thought she had, and it was with one hand over her mouth and a rather fierce look in her eyes that Graeme Hunter surprised her when he walked in from the big storeroom at the rear of the shop.

'Trouble?' he asked, taking in her attitude with a sapient glance.

'No. Just girlish bitchiness.'

He grinned. 'Find it difficult to cope with?'

'No, but I can't help wishing she wasn't a customer.'

Graeme was in his early thirties, very astute and businesslike, with a sophisticated wife and two precocious children. He had given Luce a job before she had lost her memory and kept her on, because, he said, she had a feel for old things. Between them they shared an easygoing friendship built up over the years.

Now he said quite seriously, 'Well, don't let it get the better of you. And if girlish bitchiness degenerates into abuse, give me a yell. You don't have to put up with that.'

'I know, but I doubt if Jolie can produce anything I can't handle.'

But if that was true why did she feel so angry at the other girl's disclosures?

CHAPTER THREE

ALMOST she expected to see the car waiting for her when she came out of the shop that afternoon; indeed, it was with difficulty that she prevented herself from looking up and down the street. Only the knowledge that if he was there he would see her and draw his own deductions kept her eyes straight ahead. The pang of disappointment which his absence engendered humiliated her, for it meant that the physical attraction which last night had swept her into mindlessness was stronger than she had imagined.

Did he kiss Jolie like that? At the pictures this conjured up in her brain her fingers clenched on to the strap of her handbag. Of course he did, she thought scornfully. He would not refuse what she offered, and Jolie was beautiful and hot for him. He was far too experienced not to realise that she was poised on the brink of a devastating affair. It would take only a little of the right sort of stimulation to push her into the deep end.

Rather viciously Luce found herself hoping that they both knew what they were doing and followed that up by making a vow not to have anything more to do with Conn Ramsay, who used people without scruples or mercy. If he tried to kidnap her again she would create a scene, scream, run away—do anything rather than meekly allow him to drive off so high-handedly with her. And although she had the feeling that he was a man to be intimidated by few situations, he might well draw the line at being mistaken for a kidnapper.

Her head was aching abominably by the time she reached home, so badly that she took two painkillers and went to bed.

When she awóke it was dark outside and a wind had sprung up, the keening sound of it around the windows intensely depressing. From the living room came music, and the sound of Teresa's voice, so Faith must be home. Somewhat to her surprise Luce discovered that she was hungry. Pulling a long Swiss cotton wrap over her nightgown, she padded barefoot out into the room, stopping so precipitately when she saw Conn that she almost fell over.

'Ah, you're awake,' Teresa observed cheerfully as she got up to turn the stereo down. 'Feel like something to eat now?'

'No.' Luce felt herself back away from the mocking amusement in the dark eyes fixed on her. 'I'll go and get dressed.'

'Not for my sake,' he said coolly. 'You look like a charming child.'

Teresa smiled. 'Luce is incredibly modest—we conclude that she had no brothers and sisters.'

Which was all very well for Teresa, Luce thought as she escaped back into her bedroom. Perhaps it was because both her flatmates came from large families that neither thought anything of wandering around the house in next to nothing. But she could not do it; every instinct felt outraged.

Hastily she pulled on slacks and a cotton shirt, neither in the first blush of youth, but she was not going to make any effort for him. Still, she was glad that the first shirt to come to hand was black, for it did wonderful things to her hair and skin.

When she reappeared he was talking to Teresa, effortlessly subjugating her with a charm so blatant that it should have been a carefully studied part of his manner. It wasn't, though. It was completely unconscious, as natural a part of him as the thick long lashes and the sudden warmth of his smile. There would be few people who could resist him when he chose to use this power to fascinate.

'You must have something to eat,' Teresa told her, motherly instincts temporarily taking over from those affected by an extremely personable male. 'I'll scramble you some eggs, shall I?'

Luce managed the grin that Teresa expected, for her passion for this dish was a standing joke. 'I'll do them,' she offered.

'No, you entertain our guest. This is my week for getting dinner. Conn, how about some coffee?'

'Love some.' He smiled lazily, catching Luce's hand as she walked past to pull her down beside him on to the sofa. 'I used to know someone who loved scrambled eggs.'

Breathlessly, for his hand was still around her wrist, she returned, 'Plenty of people do.'

'True. She also lusted after a *ratatouille* with an un-nerving passion.'

'I like that too.' She moved restlessly, too conscious of a latent cruelty beneath the civilised veneer. Conn wore a shirt of fine cotton and beneath the thin material his muscles moved, reminding her of the strength with which he had held her the night before.

'Am I making you uneasy?'

Surprised, she looked up, met a regard so piercing that she blinked, turning her head away. 'Yes,' she said bluntly. 'You're coming on too strong. I don't like it.'

'You enjoyed it last night.'

She jerked her wrist, but his fingers clamped on to the strong, slender bones, hurting. Between lips suddenly tight she said, 'I must have been mad. Let me go!'

'When I'm good and ready.' The green eyes taunted her; he smiled, a twisted, humourless movement of his mouth. 'Say please.'

'Conn . . .'

'Say please.'

Her anger was replaced by something more insidious: fear. It sapped her will, rendering her silent for a long moment while her eyes entreated him to release her.

They met with no response, but she knew that behind that enigmatic mask there was a keen analytical brain and that her reactions were being monitored. And she knew, as clearly as if he had shouted it at her, that he enjoyed making her feel his strength. Perhaps it was the presence of that streak of cruelty which made him such a challenge to someone like Jolie. Luce knew that it terrified her.

But she managed to break his grip, jerking her wrist sharply so that it slid through his fingers. Jumping to her feet, she put as much space between them as she could. When Teresa came in with a tray she was busy flicking through records, the clean lines of her profile hidden by the fall of her hair.

'Eat up,' Teresa ordered, setting the tray down on a low table. 'You still look a bit fragile.'

In spite of the fact that there was a flock of butterflies loose in her stomach Luce smiled. 'You'll make a wonderful mother,' she teased.

Teresa grinned, her eyes falling automatically to the cluster of diamonds which were the pledge of her love. 'Roll on the day,' she retorted lightly.

'Not a dedicated career woman?' Conn sounded ironic, his brows lifted.

'I like nursing, always have, but I'm going to enjoy being a wife and mother. As Greg is a doctor it's not going to be an easy life.'

'But the rewards will make it worthwhile.'

Apparently Teresa hadn't noticed the cynicism in his voice, for she replied happily, 'Naturally. I shouldn't be marrying if I weren't in love with him.'

'How about you, Luce?' The heavy eyelashes hid the expression in his eyes as he asked the question, but she could hear the taunt in the deep voice. 'Are you going to submerge your life in another's?'

She finished swallowing and said coldly, 'I just want to be myself.'

After a moment he said softly, 'Surely you of all

people are just that? No past to bedevil you, no memories to keep you awake at night. I know of people who would give their considerable bank accounts for a spot of amnesia.' He paused, watching her as she put her knife and fork together, then added, 'And you don't appear to grieve overmuch.'

Very conscious of Teresa's puzzled glance, Luce said slowly, 'I just want to be left alone.'

'So that you can continue to wallow in self-pity?'

Stunned, she stared at him, then a wry smile touched her lips. 'You—you *are* an arrogant brute.'

Almost she had added, 'You always were,' and her fingers flew to her lips as she stared at him in dismayed surprise.

He grinned but refused to let the subject alone. 'I wonder why women resort to personal comments when someone tells them the truth. Admit it, Luce; you rather enjoy being without a past. It gives you a hint of mystery which is incredibly intriguing.'

'What on earth makes you say so?' Teresa's bristles were well set up. She almost glared at him.

The lamplight gleamed golden on the acute angles and planes made by his features. He sat back on their shabby old sofa and dominated the room, effortlessly, as he would dominate any room. There was no reading the expression of his eyes, but the sensual mouth quirked into an enigmatic smile as he said calmly, 'The fact that she has done absolutely nothing to find out who she is.'

'The police failed. What makes you think Luce could do better?' Teresa asked rather belligerently.

His brows lifted in scepticism. 'I doubt if they made much of an effort. Why should they? Once they'd decided she wasn't an international criminal I imagine they closed her file and left it, assuming that she'd regain her memory before too long.'

'I'd just as soon you didn't talk about me as if I weren't here,' Luce said crossly. 'And for your information, Conn Ramsay, I do not make a habit of indulging in self-pity. I was perfectly happy with my life until you came along and started stirring.'

'The fact that you resent my attempts to find out what makes you tick proves my point,' he retorted with calm insolence, his glance moving over the flushed contours of her face to linger for too long on the rise and fall of her breasts.

'Wouldn't you dislike it if I pried into your innermost feelings?' she demanded, adding scornfully, 'And don't tell me your life is an open book!'

'Hardly,' he returned drily, smiling with caustic irony. 'But I can remember my past.'

'*Oh*!' Furiously angry with his constant harping on the fact of her amnesia, she scrambled to her feet, saying in a trembling voice, 'You can go to hell! I don't ever want to see you again.'

She headed for the door, but he got there before her and stopped her headlong flight by grabbing her wrists. At his touch something flared into life within her; she stood, head bent, breathing heavily while his fingers tightened.

Then she looked up. He was staring across the room at Teresa, his expression coldly intimidating. It came as no surprise when the older woman said with evident dislike of the situation, 'I'll leave you to it. Yell if you need help, Luce.'

The attempted joke fell sadly flat. Neither of them moved until she had left the room, then Conn demanded flatly, 'What the hell has happened to your manners? You should know better than to make a public spectacle of yourself.'

Mixed with the excitement which was rising through her was an anger all the stronger for being cold. 'I know Teresa far better than I know you,' she retorted with harsh distinctness. 'Blame it on the amnesia.'

'No.' He swung her around, holding her hands against his chest, his expression predatory. 'You fascinate me,' he told her coolly. 'I'm determined to find out what lies beneath that beautiful face, even if I have to hurt you to get to it.'

'I'd imagine that you'd enjoy that.'

The bitterness in her voice horrified her. It made him lift his brows, but he replied with cool control, 'Not necessarily. I'd rather make love to you than hurt you, but if pain is what is necessary, then pain it will have to be.'

'Why?'

He didn't attempt to evade the question. 'Because I'm curious.'

'So just to rid yourself of an itch of curiosity you'll tamper with my brain?'

His eyes glittered beneath the heavy lids. 'Nobody can tamper with any part of your life if you don't let them. All that I can do is make you want to emerge from this safe dark cocoon you've hidden in.' He smiled with caustic emphasis. 'Who knows, you might like what you find in the real world.'

When Luce shivered he lifted her chin, holding her trapped in the hard ruthlessness of his regard. For a long moment they stared at each other, then Conn smiled and brought his head closer so that she could feel the warmth of his breath on her mouth. A primitive hunger flamed into life, heating her skin, weakening her angry resistance with its powerful impulses.

'You frighten me,' she whispered shakily. 'You look as if you hate me.'

'Hate?' His hand moved, touched her lips, and as they trembled that hot glitter in his eyes intensified.

'I don't hate you,' he said softly. His fingers roved her face, caressing the smooth skin as if he wanted to impress the contours on his brain using every available sense. 'Don't you know the difference between hating and wanting?'

'They both frighten me.'

'I wonder why?'

Her breath caught in her throat. Held by the sensual

snare of his eyes, she felt like a rabbit entranced by a stoat, powerless, pushed by the sexual charisma of the man into a bondage more fearful than that of her empty mind.

With an effort of will so strong that it took all of her reserves of strength she began to shake her head. 'Perhaps I was raped,' she said.

Instantly the tension snapped. His hand stopped its roving to come to rest on her shoulder, pulling her close so that she rested against him in the age-old position of comfort.

'Is that what you think?'

His arm was hard across her back, his body wonderfully strong against her. She could not resist the impulse to lean against him and let him hold her as if she was a child in need of comfort.

'No, I know I haven't been. When I—when I began to get worried about what sort of person I was the doctors told me all that they knew about me. And one thing was that——' she faltered, but continued, 'well, that I was still a virgin. So I hadn't gone in for bedroom games.'

'And since then?'

Colour scalded her skin. 'No! I'm not—I don't——'

Conn laughed softly, almost a jeer into her hair.

'Your watchdogs guard you too closely, do they?'

'Don't be insolent!' Stiffening, she tried to push him away, only to discover that those strong, comforting arms could tighten into bonds of iron around her. 'How dare you!' she spat, lifting an angry, scornful face to his. 'Faith and Teresa are darlings.'

'Very protective darlings,' he agreed mockingly, making nonsense of her struggles to get free. 'So if it's not their influence which has kept you pure, it must be an inbuilt aversion to or fear of sex. Or a deep-rooted conviction that it's wrong to indulge. Let's find out which, shall we?'

Had Luce realised what he intended to do she would

have yelled for Teresa, or scratched his face—done something to escape the downward thrust of his mouth. But he seemed to have an hypnotic effect on her, eliciting confidences which she would never have dreamed of making to anyone else and stilling her instinctive withdrawal. Lulled by the lazy note in his voice, she knew her reaction came too late; she could only turn her head away, for her hands were crushed against the hard wall of his chest.

At first she thought she might avoid those questing lips, for he had only one hand free, the other splayed across her back. But he laughed, then she winced with pain as his fingers tangled in the hair at her temple. It obviously wasn't the first time he had had to subdue a woman for him to know that the delicate skin at the side of the face was infinitely more tender than at the nape.

'Keep still and you won't get hurt,' he said quietly.

She had expected the kiss to be brutal, but there was another surprise in store for her. His lips touched the corner of her mouth gently, warm and teasing, almost coaxing. Bemused, she stood still while a rising tide of excitement licked over her body, rendering her shaken yet not afraid.

'You're beautiful,' he said, punctuating each word with one of those featherlight kisses along the length of her mouth. 'Like a Norse goddess, an ice-maiden, a Valkyrie.'

'They were fairly ferocious females, if I remember right.' Was that her voice, husky and deep in her throat?

'Ah, but they could be tamed by love.' He picked her up, taking her by surprise, and carried her across to the sofa, sitting down with her across his lap so that her shoulders rested against the cushioned arms. He smiled, and bewitched by the lazy sensuality of it Luce smiled back as his hand traced out the long, lovely line of her throat, finding once more the traitorous pulse which seemed to fascinate him.

'Are you still afraid of me?'

Honesty compelled her nod. 'You know too much.'

His finger stilled. 'And what does that mean?'

'I don't know.' She reacted sharply to the quick harsh question, trying to push his hand away. In the semi-darkness of the room his features were prominent, increasing her fanciful likening of him to a hawk. He bent over her, his hand clasped around the column of her throat as if he would like to tighten his fingers and watch her writhe for breath.

For a long moment his eyes searched hers, their stabbing scrutiny a violation of her privacy. Then he relaxed as his fingers resumed their sensuous stroking.

'You make a lot of cryptic remarks,' he commented, adding with disconcerting insight, 'but I'll continue giving you the benefit of the doubt, so stop looking as though you think I'm going to strangle you.' His mouth tightened, became for an instant coldly cruel. 'When I kill you, Luce, I'll make sure that neither your lovely face nor that very sexy body are marred.'

'You like frightening me.'

His hand moved slowly from her throat to the gentle curve of her breast, rested there a moment and began its smooth exploratory sweep once more. 'You respond so satisfactorily,' he murmured, holding her eyes with his own. 'As if you were made for me.'

'Chauvinist!' But her tone lacked bite and she frowned.

'What is it?'

'Nothing.'

His fingers found the clip of her bra, twisted, and she shivered as his touch evoked a wave of sensation so intense that it was unbearable. But although he must have known what effect his practised caressing was having on her he made no reference to it.

It was a strange sensation, the mute communication of hands and body, the voices conducting a conversation on an entirely different level.

'Something bothered you,' he said softly. 'What was it?'

'*Déjà vu.* I felt as if you'd said those words to me before and I'd made the same reply.' Luce bit her lip as the erotic sensations his hands were arousing threatened to swamp her, but made no attempt to prevent him from sliding down the zip of her jeans. Their eyes were on a level and she felt drugged by the enigmatic purposefulness of his gaze; he desired her, but his desire was being made to serve his will and she did not know what he wanted of her.

'It's not an unusual comment,' he said now, softly, almost smiling. 'You may not be experienced, but this sort of thing is fairly common. The Americans call it petting. An amorous male could quite easily have felt you like this, soft and yielding, and thought that you were meant for him. And many young women consider that they owe it to their liberated ideals to toss the word chauvinist into as many conversations as possible.'

She began to tremble. Her jeans were tight, so that even with the zip down he could not explore as far as he wanted to, but his touch on her skin was incredibly erotic and when he stroked the lower part of her belly she gave a convulsive shudder, pulling herself away with an appealing look at him.

He made no attempt to stop her as she zipped herself up and pulled down the tee-shirt to hide her breasts, but his smile was sardonic and when he spoke that taunting note was back in his voice.

'I agree. This is fairly public; I acquit your friend of listening at the door, but I'll bet she's in her bedroom with her ears on the alert. And isn't your other watchdog due back soon?'

'Yes.' Luce stood, teetering between coming and going, and had her dilemma resolved when he caught her hand and pulled her down beside him. 'And don't call them watchdogs!' she continued angrily, furious at the realisation that his hand in hers and the hardness of his shoulders through several layers of clothes had the power to make her blood run so quickly. 'They've been very good to me.'

'A childish remark, but they treat you like a child, don't they?' He smiled at her outraged expression, the dark mockery antagonising her into a jerky withdrawal.

'At least they have my best interests at heart,' she said stormily from the other end of the sofa.

'And I haven't?'

She allowed her gaze to fall in a significant glance from his mouth to his hands, overcoming with an effort the vibrant excitement this gave rise to.

'I see.' He laughed, lazily and with a note of dry humour. 'You're going to have to grow up sooner or later, Luce. Why not sooner?'

'By growing up I suppose you mean that I let you seduce me?'

He leaned back on the soft cushion and let his lashes droop so that she could see nothing but the gleam of his half-closed eyes. In a painfully tolerant voice he murmured, 'Luce, if I wanted to seduce you I'd have chosen some less public place. I was conducting an experiment.'

'An—an *experiment*?' Her voice squeaked in angry shame as she stared at him, shattered.

'Exactly, sweetheart.' Subtly his voice changed, became hard and contemptuous. 'I'll tell you the results, shall I? You may not have slept with a man, but you certainly know what it's like to be made love to. Beneath that frosty veneer there's a very sensual little lady, and for your own good you'd better believe it. Otherwise one day you're going to find yourself in a situation you can't control, and I'm sure I don't have to tell you what follows on from that!'

A kind of humiliation kept her silent for a moment. Her eyes fell to her hands, clenched in her lap, the bloodless skin over her knuckles revealing the intensity

of her emotions. Slowly she relaxed them, then listened
to the wind outside wailing like a forgotten soul, as it
built up for one of the spring storms from the north-
east which brought warm rain to the red volcanic soil,
freeing the land from winter's yoke.

Aloud she said in a hard voice, 'How do you know
that it isn't just you I respond to in—in that way?'

'Are you being provocative?'

'No.' She dared not look at him; the dark features
would be tight with that smile she so disliked, that smile
which seemed a very close cousin to a sneer. 'I just don't
see that you can tell. It's like knowing whether a woman
is a virgin or not; the doctor at the hospital told me that
no man can tell. Nowadays so many women play sport
that plenty have never made love and yet are technically
not virgins. So how do you know?'

'This,' he said blandly, 'is an extremely provocative
conversation. Are you sure you want to continue?'

'You were the one who started it. I don't believe that
you know—I think it's just conceit that makes you say
you do.'

She had wanted to taunt him, to prick his pride with
her scornful comment, so it was completely disconcerting when he laughed, apparently genuinely amused, and
said with dry emphasis, 'Try your fledgling claws on
someone else, Luce. Your opinions don't worry me.
Would you like to come for a flight with me on the
weekend?'

The change of subject bewildered her, as perhaps it
was meant to. Unwillingly she turned her head to look
at him, saw him lounge with unconscious grace against
the cushions, that infuriating, mocking smile on the hard
mouth, and somewhere in the depths of her stomach
something kicked.

'I—a flight?' she asked breathlessly.

He looked bored. 'A flight. Over the area. Neither
Sonia nor Ryan can come and I'd like someone to point
out the salient features to me.'

'What about Jolie Stewart?'

Conn lifted his brows. 'What about her?'

'She knows the area better than I. Or is she unable to come again, like she was that night we went to your sister's place?'

He smiled narrowly, his unblinking glance fixed on her face. 'Is that what she told you?'

'Yes.' Already Luce regretted the impulse which had made her tell him of Jolie's hurtful remarks. A moment later she regretted it even more, for his expression hardened into a merciless mask which effectively frightened her into silence.

'Well, well, well,' he said softly as his lashes came down once more to hide his thoughts. He turned so that she saw the hard strong profile silhouetted against the golden pool of light from the lamp. Even as an old man he would be inordinately good to look at, she realised; the arrogant bony framework would not succumb to age as the softer, gentler contours of a woman's face did.

After a moment he asked, 'Well?'

'I——' she hesitated, then almost hopelessly, 'Yes, yes, I'll come.'

'Have you ever flown before?'

A dry smile touched her lips. 'I presume I arrived here by air. I'm not a New Zealander. Why?'

'It's different in a small plane.'

There was a note of—speculation, it seemed to be, in his voice, and he was once more watching her. Disregarding a cold sensation beneath her ribs, she replied curtly, having decided that she was a fool to go with him, 'I'd rather like to see the north from the air.'

She counterfeited a yawn and he smiled as he rose and took her by the hands to pull her to her feet.

'Tired?' He made it quite clear that he didn't believe her for one moment, but apparently it suited him to go then, for he picked up a jacket which he must have thrown over a chair when he came in and, still with her hand in his, urged her towards the door.

She thought he might kiss her and her heart raced within her, but he made no attempt to, smiling irony at the fleeting glance she sent him from beneath her lashes.

'Goodnight, Luce.'

Her voice was thick and husky when she responded, 'Goodnight, Conn. Drive carefully—it's going to rain any minute.'

'How solicitous of you.' For a moment they stood staring at each other until, intimidated by the cool inscrutability of his gaze, she turned away.

When Faith came in, some ten minutes later, Luce was curled up in the one comfortable armchair listening to a tape, her expression shuttered into an icy remoteness which didn't alter when the older woman spoke her name.

'Is it raining yet?' she asked.

'Any minute now. Are you all right? You look a bit drawn.'

The concern in Faith's voice would normally have warmed her. She blamed Conn with his damned insinuations for feeling slightly exasperated now.

'A headache, and Conn Ramsay's astringent company,' she replied, forcing a smile. 'For some reason he thinks that it's up to him to encourage me to regain my memory and that the best way to do it is to antagonise me into open anger.'

Faith looked across at her, a frown wrinkling her forehead. 'Well, everything else has failed, so he might be right,' she responded drily. 'How does he affect you, Luce? You seem to dislike him, but you can't be discouraging him.'

Luce permitted herself a wry smile. 'Do you honestly think that I could influence him in any way?'

'In some ways, yes.' Faith's voice became even more dry. 'You're a beautiful woman, and he's certainly very conscious of that. But I agree that he's not the most easily impressed man I know. Have you any idea why he should be so concerned?'

'I don't think he's in the least concerned. He's curious, he told me so. Perhaps he likes the idea of playing God.'

A swift frown made Faith suddenly look older, but she didn't immediately refute the suggestion. After a few moments spent considering Luce's words she said slowly, 'Perhaps, though I shouldn't have thought he would be driven by mischief, and that's what you're implying. He strikes me as a man who values his own independence too much to try to interfere in anyone else's life.'

'Yet he's doing just that.'

'Yes.' The dark eyes were reflective as they dwelt on Luce's hands, slender and restless against the dark denim of her jeans. 'Perhaps he really does want to use your experiences. Or perhaps . . .' Her voice trailed away in unusual hesitation. After several moments she resumed, 'I think it would be very difficult for Conn to refuse a challenge.'

Luce looked at her in astonishment. 'And I am one?'

'Oh yes. You're cool and self-contained. Some men find that very challenging. I shouldn't have thought that Conn was one of them, but you never know.'

A shiver ran across Luce's skin. Compressing her lips, she said in hard tones, 'He wants me to go on a flight around the harbour, with him.'

'Are you going?'

Sighing, she answered, 'Yes.'

'Are you sure that you know what you're doing?'

'No.' Luce would have given much to be able to confide in Faith, but the older woman's kind common sense was no armour against Conn's dark attraction. After a moment she said huskily, 'I don't even like him.'

'You're going to get hurt,' Faith said worriedly. 'And what about Jolie?'

'What about her?'

'Well, she does rather seem to have staked a claim.'

Luce laughed, the clear notes humourless. 'Nobody stakes a claim to Conn,' she stated, knowing the truth of it. 'And he stakes no claims himself. Totally self-sufficient, that's him. Jolie may be his mistress, but if she tries to make him jealous he'll turn his back on her with a smile.'

She was shaking, her hands clasped so tightly in her lap that they seemed locked together.

'How do you know?' When she didn't answer Faith repeated sharply, 'Luce, how do you know? Have you met him before—do you know him? Luce, have you remembered?'

A pressure at the back of her eyes made them ache, but although Luce expected them no tears came. Harshly she answered, 'No, I've never seen him before. He told me that I didn't know him.'

'Then what are you worrying about?' Faith came across, touched her shoulder gently, her kind blunt features revealing her concern.

'I'm not.' Luce took a deep breath, forcing herself into a semblance of composure. After a moment she continued, 'I must have known somebody like him, I suppose. He—he has no reason to lie to me.'

'No, of course not, although I can see him lying without turning a hair if he thought it necessary. If he really is interested in helping you regain your memory and does know you then he would tell you, I'm sure. Talking over old times would possibly be a great help.'

Luce nodded, obscurely driven to defend him. 'Why do you say you could see him lying?'

'My dear, there's very little he's incapable of doing, and maybe even murder. You know it, although you might not like it. The violence and recklessness are held in severe check, but they're there.' Faith yawned, then smiled. 'It's part of the reason why he's so exciting. That's what Jolie is hooked on. That's why I think you'd do better to keep him at a distance.'

'I suppose so.' Yawns are infectious; Luce hid hers

with her hand as she rose to her feet, swaying slightly. 'Well, I'll go flying with him and then make it quite clear that I don't want to see any more of him.'

It was impossible to see properly in the shadowed room, but Faith's gaze seemed compassionate as she said lightly, 'You do that, Luce. If he's the sort of man you think him he'll turn away with a smile, won't he?'

CHAPTER FOUR

SATURDAY was perfect for sightseeing, clear and sunny with a gentle wind, the only clouds great high galleons over the hills in the centre of the island. Luce ate breakfast pensively, wondering why there was an unpleasantly cold area in the pit of her stomach.

'Another cup of coffee?' Teresa filled the pottery mug and pushed it across the table. 'Getting cold feet?'

'Very much so.'

The two other women exchanged glances, but neither of them said anything, for which Luce was grateful. She knew that they worried about her relationship with Conn. She wasn't exactly happy about it herself, but she could not explain to them the reason why she hadn't told him to leave her alone. She could not explain it to them because she did not know herself what power he wielded, only that it was one she could resist but not overcome.

Physical attraction, she told herself, and indeed her blood seemed to fire with excitement and hunger whenever she saw him, but there was more to it than mere sexual magnetism. He drew her with a fiercer, darker desire, and that was why she was afraid of him. If it was merely a mutual passion it would be easy enough to sate herself. He would not refuse her if she made her desire obvious, for he wanted her too. But there were other instincts and needs as well as the sexual, and she was afraid that when he saw her it was as the personification of urges he despised and wished to be purged from.

He came before they had finished their meal, a disturbing, immensely attractive man in a polo-necked shirt that clung to the powerful muscles of his shoulders and chest.

'Ready, Luce?'

She made a play for independence. 'I'll finish my coffee. Would you like some?'

'No,' he said, and that was all, but she set her mug down and turned to get her blazer, obeying his unspoken command even as it chilled her.

Once in the car he slanted a sideways glance at her. 'You look very fetching, although your clothes have a distinctly nautical air. I gather your friends don't approve of this jaunt.'

'Too astute by half, you are. What else can you expect?'

Conn grinned. 'Do they think I have designs on your person?'

'Have you?'

'Any number,' he told her calmly. 'But I think I can manage to control my raging lust while we're in the plane.'

A dimple quivered beside her mouth as she subdued a desire to giggle. He didn't miss it, of course; she began to think that he was able to see with his skin.

'I like that dimple. You must have made an enchanting schoolgirl.'

'I doubt it,' Luce said on a half sigh. 'All legs and arms, I'll bet, with an infuriating giggle and hair in pigtails.'

He laughed outright at that, suddenly revealing a new Conn, infinitely more approachable than the old, and for the rest of the short drive out to the airport he made her laugh too, imagining a schoolgirl past for her which involved several elements of St Trinian's, but much more of a vein of immensely likeable idiocy in his makeup.

The wind seemed to freshen as they climbed the hill to Onerahi, but the gardens about the neat suburb were not being tossed too violently, so Luce forced herself to relax, aware of that ominous cold patch in her midriff once more.

'You've gone all silent,' he commented as he turned the car towards the airport.

'I'm beginning to wonder if I'm afraid of flying.'

He said nothing, but when the car had been parked and she was standing beside it, one hand at the blue scarf which hid the bright fall of her hair, he asked, 'And do you think you are?'

'There's only one way to find out.'

For a moment there was something like respect in the green-brown gaze which scanned her face; before Luce had a chance to know for certain his heavy lids hid the expression and he said coolly, 'Well, let's go.'

She should not have been astonished to realise that he intended to pilot the little Cessna himself, for he had that air of being able to do anything, but she was, and it showed.

'I'm qualified,' he taunted softly.

'I believe you.'

A knot of tension tightened in her stomach. As they went through the pre-flight procedures she forced herself to breathe deeply and found to her relief that concentration on that and the deliberate relaxation of her muscles banished that kick of fear.

And when they had left the ground she slipped sunglasses on to hide any residual tension and looked out, awed by the beauty of the scene below. In the crisp spring sunlight Whangarei lay at the head of the drowned river valley which was its harbour, a collection of vividly coloured roofs against the even more vivid green of the subtropical growth. The city grew in tendrils along valleys hemmed in by the Western Hills and the forested volcanic cone of Parahaki with its obelisk. Above the long chimney of the oil refinery to the south a perpetual flame burnt; beside the complex was the power station with its candy-striped stacks dominating the small town of Ruakaka. On the other side of the harbour loomed the jagged improbable peaks of the Whangarei Heads, high volcanic teeth impudently topped by the white and black cone of a trig height.

'It must have been quite a job hauling that up the cliff,' Luce commented, aware that he was watching her closely.

'Tough men, in those days.'

Even tougher now, she thought.

She was kept busy pointing out landmarks, sometimes finding it difficult to discern where they were as from this strange angle the topography looked different. To their right the Pacific Ocean rolled against the coastline, the surface of it wrinkled and lazy and incredibly blue, and where the sea met the land were beaches, harbours and estuaries, Pataua, Ngunguru, Tutukaka, and Matapouri, the euphonious Maori names now tripping easily off her tongue as she pointed them out, her love for this long, northern peninsula very evident.

'In summer there are hordes of people here,' she told Conn. 'They come for surfing and big game fishing; a lot go out to the Poor Knights Islands, over there on our right, to dive. There are tropical fish brought down by a warm current. They say it's beautiful.'

Perhaps her voice had held a note of unconscious wistfulness, for he asked, 'Have you not gone skin-diving?'

'No, it's an expensive hobby. Have you?'

'Yes. I'll take you, some day.'

She smiled. 'How long are you planning to stay?'

'As long as it takes,' he said ambiguously, and when she snorted lifted a mocking eyebrow at her. 'You've learned to love this country.'

'It's the only one I know.' A thin thread of desolation in her voice made her sound self-pitying. She straightened up, added with a briskness she was far from feeling, 'It's beautiful—wild and free and romantic. It has a landscape as varied as any you could find. You never get bored driving around here because you don't know what's going to happen around the next corner.'

He smiled. 'I can see that. I'm going up to the Bay of

Islands tomorrow. Care to come with me?'

Now was the time to tell him that she didn't want to have anything more to do with him. It helped to imagine Jolie's sullen beauty as she had made sure that Luce knew she was second best.

'I'm going to be busy tomorrow,' she said, forcing her voice to sound firm, almost hard.

'Really?' Conn didn't sound in the least upset, adding blandly, 'Another time, perhaps.'

See, it was easy, Luce told herself, staring with blind eyes at the green and blue beneath. A few more rebuffs and he would not come again, she was sure of it. Self-sufficiency was the name of the game; had anyone asked her she was prepared to bet that Conn would never fight for her—or any woman's company. Possessed of that private and personal magnetism, he had probably had to fend women off all his adult life, and there was nothing other than the easing of physical tension that he wanted from them.

His plays revealed the real Conn Ramsay—so deeply cynical that to him even humanity's finest actions were ultimately based on self-interest. For the moment he found her interesting, but it was not Luce Laurenson who held his attention, it was the aberrations of her mind and the contours of her body.

And you'd better not ever forget it, she told herself, wishing that she could introduce him to the beauties of the Bay of Islands, that exquisite region where at the end of the last ice age the rising sea had drowned an ancient river valley, producing a deeply indented bay. Like jewels on silk, it was scattered with a hundred and fifty islands, some no more than rocks, others big enough to be farmed.

Luce remained silent, and as it was time to go down neither spoke until the little plane came to a halt on the short wiry grass. Then she gave a curious sigh and fainted dead away.

Conn's voice was the first thing that impinged on her

returning consciousness. He was swearing softly, viciously, as he pulled at the safety-belt trying to free her. For a moment everything whirled hideously. Nausea clogged her throat, but after swallowing once or twice the world settled down and she opened her eyes.

Returning blood heated her face like the effects of a blow as she muttered, 'It's all right. I'm so sorry.'

'So I should think!' He was too close for comfort, the flames leaping in the hard green eyes as they scanned her face. 'What the hell happened?'

'I don't know.' She watched as his lean hands unbuckled the safety-belt, felt a faint stirring in her blood and damped it down, moistening her lips nervously. 'I just passed out with the minimum of fuss.'

'Are you all right now?'

'Yes, I feel fine.'

'Wait there, and I'll help you down.'

Distinctly wobbly as her legs felt, she needed the support. When they reached the ground Conn held her against him, his arms tight across her back, giving support without any sexual awareness until she sighed and pulled away, afraid that she betrayed too clearly her pleasure at his closeness.

'Think you can get to the car?'

The curtness of his voice prompted her quick withdrawal. 'Yes, of course,' she replied in a remote voice.

'Here are the keys. You'd better wait in it until I get there.'

Luce caught the tossed keys, walked back across the grass to the car park. High above a skylark sang his heart out, every note crystal clear, rising and falling like a paean of praise to the day. The breeze was cool, from the south but without winter's bitterness, and in its passage over the harbour it picked up a salt tang. To the south and west lay green farmlands where purple cloud shadows chased each other across the fertile contours of the land. Luce looked for the distant Brynderwyn Hills and followed the grape blue outline down to the coast.

Somewhere down there was Waipu Cove, where she had first set eyes on Conn. From that first electric moment she had known that he was going to be significant in her life. As her eyes roamed the islands, from the sharp triangle of Sail Rock to the Hen and Chickens, she found herself wondering just how significant he was going to be.

'I told you to get in and sit down!'

His silent approach from behind startled her. Without taking her eyes from the scene before her she said huskily, 'I love this place. It satisfies me.'

'A good spring day is like a benediction,' he agreed. 'You surprise me.'

'Why?'

He smiled, not very pleasantly, and took the keys from her, keeping hold of her hand when she would have twisted it away. Over her dark blue slacks and the blue and white striped cotton knit camisole which he had called nautical she wore a white blazer. Against it his hand was tanned; she stood almost submissively, her head bent as she kept her eyes on the strong fingers, wondering where he had got that tan. The northern summer must have been a good one.

'Because you look a sophisticated, perfected work of art,' he said quietly, each word cool and distinct and emotionless. 'You have a remote delicacy which doesn't fit in with this distinctly rural, almost primitive setting. You're the product of a super-civilised environment; you belong to the city. What brought you to this little town?'

'Who knows?' She forced a flippant note into her voice. 'This is where I found myself when I woke up. And here I've stayed. It's not entirely without cultural amenities, you know.'

'So Sonia informs me.' His hand tipped her chin so that she found herself looking at him through the tips of her lashes, noting the strong lines and planes of his face, the hint of recklessness in the sensual mouth, the lines of self-control that overrode it.

'Tell me about it,' he said, his glance probing as if he wanted her brain spread out before him.

'About what?'

'Where you were when you woke up. How you felt. You'd been in Whangarei for some time, hadn't you, before the accident which led to your loss of memory?'

'Some weeks.' She freed herself, leaned back against the bonnet to search for the lark in the clear sky, her eyes shadowed. 'Long enough to get my job in the shop but not enough to have found a place to live. I was still in a private hotel.'

'Tell me exactly what happened.'

Luce sighed. If recounting the events which had led up to the fall had had any chance of bringing her memory back it would have returned long since, but obediently she recapitulated. 'Apparently I'd been at work and come home with a magazine. I was reading it as I climbed the stairs. I tripped and fell and knocked myself unconscious. I didn't recover immediately, so they took me to hospital. When I did come to I couldn't remember who I was. And that was that.'

'Was the magazine checked to see whether there was anything in it that could have had a bearing on the business?'

She shrugged. 'Yes. In fact, I think I've still got it somewhere, but it's just an ordinary glossy magazine, fashions, an article on antiques, several on people of note—the usual things. Nothing that could possibly have shocked my subconscious into burying the past.'

The flippancy in her tones might have irritated him, for he sent her a swift, hard glance, but said nothing. After a moment she continued defiantly, 'To be quite honest I'm sick of the whole business. I just want to be left alone to live my perfectly ordinary life, not exhibited as some kind of freak. You'd be surprised how many people think that amnesia means either that you're half-witted or mad—or a combination of both.'

Anger brought a sparkle to the grey depths of her eyes, lending her expression a kind of fierceness that animated her whole countenance. For a moment she looked at Conn as though she would like to hit him, but the impulse died as soon as it was born and, trembling, she turned away, aware that she had revealed just how much her loss of memory nagged her.

'I can promise you that I think you neither,' he said calmly. 'Does it really matter what people think?'

'It does when they transmute their thoughts into action.' A sudden spurt of laughter replaced the stormy expression of a moment ago. 'Not so long after I came out of hospital I went to a dinner party with Teresa and the hostess told me, in a very sibilant whisper, not only the name of each dish but which cutlery to use!'

He grinned. 'How did you cope?'

'I was furious at first, but after a couple of courses my sense of humour got the better of me and I had to stifle the worst fit of the giggles I've ever had. By the time we went home Teresa and I were nearly hysterical.' She chuckled, adding, 'People think the oddest things, but by and large they've been quite incredibly kind. Almost to a fault.'

'New Zealanders are inclined to be overwhelming,' he agreed, somewhat drily. 'The kind of hospitality that's generous yet without pretension. Fortunately Sonia filters all my calls and assures everyone that I'm extremely busy writing a play.'

'Are you?'

His glance was sardonic. 'Oh yes, it's true. Sonia doesn't lie.'

'Somehow I imagined that you'd retire into your shell while you're working. You know, the mad genius who mustn't be disturbed.'

'With keepers who tiptoe in while I'm asleep and lift the day's efforts before I shred them in my maniacal fury?'

She laughed, her soft amusement disturbing the remote mask of her features. She felt vividly, vitally alive and knew that it was more than physical attraction which tugged at her. The lark had finished singing and there was only the faint hum of a speedboat in the harbour to blend with the soft sound of the wind; all about her a bubble of delight formed, round and fragile and beautiful, enclosing the two of them in an enchanted iridescence.

'You're beautiful,' he said, and when she looked up at him without astonishment he lifted his hand and touched her breast where her heart beat heavily within her. His fingers separated, splaying out across the stretch towelling of her camisole, displaying his expertise and his experience in the way they caressed the most sensitive areas while he looked down at her with mocking eyes, daring her to protest.

'No prudish demands for me to stop?'

She bit her lips to stop them revealing how much she wanted him. 'It would be a waste of time, wouldn't it?'

His glance sharpened. 'So if I decided to take you you'd make no resistance?'

'Ah, that's a different thing.' Colour washed over her face and throat, but she kept her glance steady, feeling like a mouse in the sights of a hovering bird of prey. 'I think my instinct of self-preservation would prevent me from being quite so reckless.'

Laughter gleamed in the hooded eyes as his hand slid up to rest across her throat, pinning her against the car. 'If you had any instinct of self-preservation you'd have left town the day you saw me,' he said softly. And then with a suddenness that startled her he let her go, turning away as he ordered, 'Get in, it's time to go.'

Once in the confines of the car the awareness which made her uncomfortable became intensified; she was glad that he made no conversation on the way home. The careless ease with which he had handled her made her angry now. She did not need to look at the hard

aquiline profile to know that he had put that casual
desire from him and was now giving his entire concentration to his driving. Pride insisted that she refuse to
become a toy for his leisure hours. And when the deeper,
darker reaches of her personality whispered that pride
was a cold bedfellow she ignored the seductive suggestion. Somewhere was imprinted the knowledge that he
could destroy her, casually, effortlessly, and go his way
unmarked by the experience. If he wanted a holiday
romance let him seduce Jolie Stewart, she thought
waspishly.

At the door of the flat he refused her offer of coffee,
but when she turned away he said harshly, 'You should
learn to hide your relief, Luce,' and pulled her into his
arms and kissed her, holding her with his hands and his
mouth, pressing her against the door so that she was
trapped between it and the hard contours of his body.

'Kiss me,' he said against her mouth.

She could not shake her head, but her wide, defiant gaze
refused him, forcing him to realise that his strength could
enforce his will but would evoke no response
from her. And yet, while his angry, arrogant mouth claimed hers that wellspring of delight which had come into
being when she heard the lark sprang into fuller flow,
sending currents of singing desire along her nerves and
veins so that she had to close her eyes to hide their
expression.

'Why do you fight me?' he asked against her mouth.
'You took one look at me and decided that if you never
saw me again it would be too soon. Why, Luce?'

'I don't know.' His mouth moved with seductive
slowness across the line of her jaw; she tightened every
muscle in mute resistance, and he laughed and drew
away.

'You do know, darling, and when you admit it life
will be much simpler for us both. Goodbye.'

Belatedly she thanked him for the flight, met the sardonic laughter in his glance with as much self-possession

as she could and did not breathe easily until his car had pulled away.

Teresa was reposing on a towel on the back lawn, clad in a bikini so minuscule that it was barely decent.

'Nonsense,' she retorted when Luce told her so. 'Anyway, there's no one to see. Everyone has gone to the beach. Did you have a good time?'

'Yes.'

'You sound surprised.' She sat up, holding her bikini bra in place, and surveyed Luce's expression. 'You don't like the man, do you?'

'Oh, I like him,' Luce told her gloomily. 'I just don't trust him.'

'But, Luce, even the nicest man can't be trusted. They'll all try to get you into bed—it's normal.'

Luce laughed, pulling off the scarf which had held her hair in place. 'You come out with the most cynical observations with such wide-eyed innocence. Did your beloved try?'

'Of course he did.' A faint blush made Teresa suddenly shy. 'As I said, they all do. Why, is the handsome brute putting the hard word on you?'

'No.' Luce shook her hair free, running her fingers through its soft silkiness as she relaxed on to the aged deck chair which was their only piece of outdoor furniture. 'Not yet. I think he's trying to tip me off balance.'

'And succeeding, by the looks of it.'

The soft swathe of hair fell forward as Luce nodded. 'I'm afraid so. He's attractive, of course, but there's more to it than that . . .' As her voice trailed away she sighed rather forlornly.

'Like what?'

'I don't really know.' She stirred uneasily, trying to put into order her vague inchoate suspicions and fears. 'Well, for one thing, I don't think he likes me. I know he's not your average guy, but even so it's peculiar for a man to pursue someone he despises. He says he's interested in the amnesia, but he could find out more about it from a good book, or a psychiatrist.'

'Yes, but couldn't he be interested in your reactions to it?'

'I suppose so, but I have no reactions. I mean, I accept it. I don't go around bursting into tears or suffering or throwing out mysterious hints, or having breakdowns.' Luce pushed a hand across her forehead, unable to put into words the strange dread which Conn Ramsay inspired in her. 'I just live,' she said defiantly. 'A perfectly ordinary, normal life. And I defy anyone, however talented or brilliant, to find much inspiration in that!'

'That's nonsense, and you know it,' Teresa told her briskly. 'Look at *Death of a Salesman* and *Main Street* and hundreds of other plays, all about ordinary people. And that's only plays. No, I think he could be gathering material. But he's obviously interested in you too. Let's fact it, Luce, you're a very sexy lady, if you like ladies with hints of fire beneath the snow. I've seen the way he looks at you and there's very definite masculine appreciation there.' She hesitated, tied the straps of her bra about her and went on slowly, 'That night he ordered me out of the room . . .'

'Yes.'

'Did anything happen?'

'Did he make love to me, you mean?' Luce shrugged. 'He kissed me, then told me it was an experiment and that I'd obviously had some experience.'

'Did he really?' Teresa looked her incredulity. 'What a beast! Did you enjoy it?'

'Oh, I liked it. At least—I find him immensely attractive.' Luce composed her expression into one of simpering idiocy and said with self-mocking emphasis, 'He makes my heart go thump in my bosom and my spine tingles. But I still don't trust him.'

'Do you think you have the same effect on him?'

A faint blush touched the pale skin across Luce's cheekbones. 'Oh yes, I think so,' she said gently, remembering the thickened note in his voice, the hunger which even so experienced a man as he couldn't hide.

'Then you could be in trouble,' said Teresa, climbing to her feet. 'Because I have the feeling that what that man wants, that man gets. Although he has the sort of willpower that hits you in the eyes, so he might be able to resist your considerable appeal.'

'Let's just hope that he draws the line at seducing amnesiacs.' Luce's voice was deliberately frivolous, but to her surprise Teresa took her seriously, nodding.

'I think you might appeal to his protective instincts,' she said.

'If he's got any.'

'Oh, strong men are usually protective even if it doesn't show. Protective or possessive. I rather suspect the fascinating Conn to be both. Gosh, I'm dying of thirst!'

Luce got to her feet. 'I'll make some coffee.'

'Lovely. Oh, the mail is here, by the way. There's something for you—an invitation, by the look of it.'

It was an invitation. Luce read it in astonishment, then flipped it across to her companion.

'Good lord!' Teresa read it through again. 'Jolie Stewart, of all people, inviting you to her twenty-first! Now why should she do that? She doesn't even know you, really.'

'I suppose it has something to do with Conn,' Luce said drily as she made the coffee.

'But what?'

'I don't know.'

'Are you going?'

Luce smiled. 'Hardly. As you said, I barely know her, and I'm damned if I'm going to be patronised by her. I've no doubt her birthday party will be a howling success without my presence.'

'Mmm, I see your point, but it's a pity. You'd really see how the other half lives. Jolie moved in the very best circles. At least,' Teresa added scrupulously and not a

little cattily, 'her parents do. I think our Jolie is rather
making a name for herself as a permissive lady. I wonder
why she asked you, though. Do you think Conn can
have asked her to?'

'Hardly. He has no reason to. I don't even know if
he's going.'

'Oh, bound to. The McLeods and the Stewarts came
out on the same boat, so his sister will be going.'

Luce nodded, but found herself wondering whether
even Sonia and the inscrutable Ryan could make Conn
do something if he didn't want to. But why should she
think he wouldn't want to go to Jolie's party? He'd
probably have himself a marvellous time, she thought
maliciously, dazzling every woman in sight with that
brand of masculine attraction he'd made especially his
own.

When Faith arrived home she was told immediately
by Teresa about the invitation, but beyond favouring
Luce with a cool considering glance she said very little,
neither urging her to accept as Teresa was almost doing
or supporting her decision to refuse.

With every intention of refusing Luce somehow found
herself back at work on Monday, with her answer un-
written.

It seemed like a conspiracy when Sonia McLeod came
in, jean-clad and almost harassed, with a small, alarmingly truculent girl attached to one hand.

'No, darling, you are not going to the movies,' she
said, and there must have been something in the tone of
her voice which meant business, for the child stopped
playing up and became just as alarmingly demure.

'How did you do it?' Luce's voice was awed.

A grin, mischievous and not a little smug, made Sonia
suddenly much younger. 'Native ability and the threat
of her father,' she said frivolously, adding with a swift
cuddle for the child, 'But Melissa is very reasonable,
even though she has her father's iron will. Thank the
powers that be, both of the kids are. Now, I've come to

thank you for suggesting that beautiful vase to Conn. I love it.'

'I'm so glad.' It was impossible to be stiff with Sonia. She had such warm eyes that they impelled confidence. Luce could understand why Ryan McLeod, cold and hard and self-sufficient, loved her. Her warmth and compassion, her kindness and generosity of spirit would attract him. They were the two halves of a whole.

Impulsively, without any of her usual caution Luce said, 'It's the oddest thing, but I've had an invitation from Jolie Stewart to her party. I can't think why she should want me to come.'

Surprise flashed into the older woman's expressive eyes. 'Well, no,' she agreed, adding with a chuckle, 'She's not normally keen on competition, poor Jolie. Are you going?'

'No. I don't know her—or her family—at all. It's a real puzzle to me why she sent me an invitation.'

'Oh, why don't you go? The Stewarts are a charming couple and the party is guaranteed to be a success.' Sonia's face lit up with enthusiasm. 'I know, come out and stay the night with us and we'll all go together!'

Too late Luce saw the pit her unwary confidence had dug for her. 'Oh no . . .' she stammered, wishing that she had had the sense to stay quiet. 'No, it's very kind of you, but I couldn't impose—I've decided to refuse the invitation.'

'A pity.' But Sonia, although regretful, didn't urge her to reconsider, beyond saying, 'If you do change your mind, I'll be upset if you don't go with us. It's always more fun to go with someone you know, and Ryan is never averse to escorting a beautiful woman.'

Luce flushed, but said lightly, 'A beautiful woman? It would be two, surely.'

'Sweet of you, my dear, but the best you can say for me is that I have a certain charm and attraction.'

'Your husband thinks you're beautiful.'

Sonia smiled. 'Yes, I know,' she said softly.

Envy hurt, Luce discovered. It was a heavy weight in her breast as she bade Sonia and her daughter goodbye, and it had not gone by the end of the day when she called a farewell to Graeme. The less she saw of Sonia McLeod the better, she decided as she walked home in the warm evening. There had been that in the older woman's voice when she spoke of her husband which had reminded Luce only too strongly that for her there was no lover, no man who saw through the superficial beauty of skin and bone structure and colouring and thought that what was beneath was beautiful.

Somehow she doubted that she would ever be able to become so vulnerable, so open to hurt as to love another person with the ardour that she had glimpsed for a brief moment in Sonia's eyes.

Because the subject made her melancholy she banished it from her mind, but it had reinforced her decision not to go to the party, and that night she wrote her refusal and left it on the table in the tiny hall to be posted next day.

'I think you should go, you know,' Teresa said when she saw it there.

'I might, if I'd someone to go with.' Luce hadn't mentioned Sonia's proposal and took refuge in a half lie when she saw that the other girl was prepared to press the issue.

'Fair enough, I suppose.' Teresa's chuckle was wickedly sly. 'You could, of course, see if Conn is prepared to squire you.'

'No. I don't think I'll be seeing much of him from now on.'

'Well, he's just pulled up outside, so you're going to see something of him right now.' Teresa was going out; as she picked up her bag she said swiftly, 'You'll be O.K.? I mean, I can stay in.'

'Rubbish!' Luce's voice expressed a confidence she was far from feeling. 'Go and have a nice dinner with the Moores. He's not likely to beat me up or rape me.'

'No such luck!'

Which meant that Teresa certainly didn't think him capable of such violence. Luce was not quite so sure. He was always well in command of himself, presenting a tough mocking mask to the world, but beneath that mask there were some very strong passions. It might take a lot to make him lose control, but if ever he did she didn't want to be around when it happened.

He and Teresa met at the door; she could hear their voices, his lazy, humorous, Teresa's answering laugh, then there was a moment of silence before he came into the living room.

'Hi,' she said, above the hammering of her heart.

'Hi.' He was dressed in jeans and a dark shirt, and his expression was watchful and enigmatic as he looked at her, curled up on the sofa, her legs gleaming with the first of the summer tan beneath old denim shorts.

'You look very fetching,' he said as he came into the room and dropped down beside her. 'Have you been gardening?'

His finger traced a thin scratch on her thigh while the bright mockery of his gaze took in the sudden flush which heated her face.

'Just a vagrant piece of wistaria,' she said, and got to her feet, desperate to put some distance between them.

He knew, of course. Without altering his expression he put out a hand and caught her wrist. She stopped, looking down at the dark crown of his head and the strong bones of nose and cheek as he bent forward and pressed his lips to the scratch. An agony of desire shook her; she almost cried out at the sensations his mouth on her leg gave rise to. Her teeth came down to clamp on to her bottom lip while she stood stock still, terrified at the depths of her need. After a moment she felt with something like anguish the tip of his tongue follow the line of the abrasion, and then she was free, and nothing in her life was ever going to be the same again.

'Stay away from the wistaria,' he ordered, smiling, his glance fierce and hot on her face. 'I don't like my possessions flawed, or marked by anything but me.'

'Am I your possession?' she asked harshly.

'Oh, I think so.' He was very sure of himself, tough and cynical and experienced, and when she said nothing he smiled again and pulled her down on to his knees, holding her still until she stopped struggling. Then he said calmly, 'Perhaps not just yet, but it won't be long before you are. You're not stupid; you know I want you.'

'Don't my wishes count for anything?'

'Fighting a desperate rearguard action?' A black brow lifted satirically. 'I've never been afflicted with the English love for lost causes. If there's no prospect of winning I prefer not to play. We both knew, right from the moment we set eyes on each other, that this is where we were headed. And if I'd been in any doubt at all your response to the lures I've tossed in your direction would have convinced me.'

Luce was shaking her head, and he put his hand up and touched the nape of her neck, threading his fingers through the soft silk of her hair. His touch was gentle, and although she knew he was wrong, she shivered and turned her hot face into the warm column of his throat.

The deep voice said quietly, 'You come to life when I touch you, Luce. Don't try to lie to me.'

'Of course you know all about it, you've had a vast amount of experience,' she snapped, panic driving her to her feet in one swift movement.

It took him by surprise. Eyes narrowed as he watched her pace across the room to stand by the french doors which led to the minuscule terrace.

'You may not have had as much experience, but you're not as innocent as those virginal looks would have people believe,' he said after a moment, his voice almost bored. 'So why the panic?'

If she told him that he could destroy her he would laugh, and indeed, it was too dramatic to be sensible. But she knew that he could, that there was something about him which made every instinct she possessed afraid. He wanted an affair and Jolie was too obvious to appeal to him, so he had decided on her, and if she let him make love to her she would be lost in the dark abyss which threatened her.

'I'm just not geared for affairs,' she said quietly. 'I don't want to be hurt.'

'Why are you so sure it would hurt? We're good together; that experience you're so scathing about will ensure that your initiation will be enjoyable.'

'I didn't mean that sort of pain, and you know it.' She spoke bitterly, aware that they had no meeting ground. He was sophisticated, a worldly man with a cynical outlook on relationships between the sexes. He thought her prudish, stupidly so, and any attempt to make him appreciate her fears and doubts was doomed to failure.

'How many women have you loved?'

The question brought a cool, speculative smile to his lips. 'I'm no sexual athlete,' he said drily. 'If by loved you mean gone to bed with, I don't make notches on the bedpost. But if you mean the grand passion the poets babble of then I'd have to tell you that the answer is none. I gave up expecting or wanting that ten years ago. The concept of romantic love is probably directly responsible for more unhappiness today than any other idea, and I've no intention of offering a sacrifice on its altar.'

'Why don't you write a play about it?' she asked, weariness dulling her voice, then before he had a chance to respond, 'Oh, Conn, please believe me when I say I don't want to—to get involved—with anyone at all.'

His glance had been mocking, a taunt without words, but when she said this it sharpened, became fiercely focussed on her face as though he was trying to see through the outer covering to the brain beneath.

'Why?' When she didn't answer he repeated, 'Why, Luce? Why are you so afraid of involvement, of becom-

ing attached to anyone? Your friends tell me that you've
gone out with plenty of men, but as soon as they show
signs of becoming serious you back away as if you're
afraid of any emotional entanglement, however mild.
Why do you keep men at a distance, Luce? You're not
afraid of all emotion—you've allowed yourself to
become very fond of Faith and Teresa. Why does the
thought of allowing a man close to you frighten you?'

The direct attack angered her. 'I suppose all play-
wrights fancy themselves as psychologists,' she snapped,
turning away so that he couldn't see the pallor of her
face. 'Why don't you tell me, seeing you know so much
about me?'

'Oh, I've several theories.' Conn got up and came
towards her, stopping to stand a few inches behind her.
'But I'll keep them to myself for now. Did you accept
Jolie's invitation?'

She swung round, her expression startled as she met
the cool query in his glance. 'I—it's none of your business.'

'I've just made it mine. I'll bet you've written her a
formal refusal.'

'And if I have?'

'It reinforces my contention that you're a coward.'
Conn grinned and strode across to where the envelope
rested on the small table.

When Luce realised that he was going to open it she
made a dash for it, but he stopped her by the simple
expedient of hauling her against him with an arm which
felt like a steel cable and holding her there.

'Let me go!' she panted, her fury at his arrogance
undermining her caution. 'Don't you dare—oh!' She
writhed uselessly until the gleam beneath his lashes
warned her that her struggles to free herself were having
an unforeseen effect on him. Mutinously she met his
glance with contempt, trying to hide the fact that her
own pulses were leaping in time to a suddenly frantic
heartbeat.

'Must you stop?' he enquired smoothly. 'Just when it was getting interesting, too.'

'Snake!'

Not at all upset by the loathing she managed to invest in the word, he read her carefully written refusal before crushing it in his hand and letting it fall to the ground.

'Why did you do that?' Luce could have raked her fingernails down his handsome face with immense pleasure. 'Conn, I don't want to go to her party! I don't even know why she asked me. And——'

'She asked you because I let it be known, without ever saying so, that unless you were there I wouldn't be.' He grinned derisively at her flushed, furious face. 'And you are going, my sweet, either willingly or because I'll come and get you myself.'

'Don't be an idiot! You can't force me to——'

'No?' The laughter disappeared from his expression leaving it coldly remorseless. 'Oh, I think I could,' he said quietly.

Luce's brain told her that there was no way he could make her go, but she shivered at the expression on his face and tried to step backwards. Instantly his arm tightened. It was very quiet. The evening rush of traffic had faded, and the only noise from the street was the sound of someone whistling a long way away. Down at the far end of the street a mother called her child, for while they had talked the sun had disappeared behind the bushclad slopes of the Western Hills and the dew had started to fall.

Inside the room, motionless, the two people fought a battle all the fiercer for being completely silent. Luce tried to drag her eyes from Conn's, determined not to let herself be intimidated into giving in, but he refused to allow her until at last she closed her eyes, covering pupils which had suddenly become hot and tired.

'I could, couldn't I, Luce?' he said.

A deep breath lifted her breasts. 'No,' she whispered, trying to ignore the hard strong lines of his body against hers. She knew what he was doing, of course, and knew too that intensely disturbing as she found his physical closeness he was affected by hers as much.

'Luce?' His mouth was warm against her ear, the deep tones of his voice softening. 'You look like an ice maiden, but your mouth and eyes give the lie to that. Are you going to accept that invitation?'

His habit of changing the subject surprised her once more. She was angry, with him for using the oldest method of persuasion in the book, and with herself for not being immune to the touch of his hands across her back, the erotic magic of his voice and his eyes and the elusive male scent of him.

'No,' she said clearly, defiantly.

He laughed, and tipped her chin up. 'Good,' he murmured outrageously. 'I'm going to enjoy convincing you that it's the wisest thing to do.'

CHAPTER FIVE

LUCE tried to pull away, but the hands which had been so gentle became cruel fetters, forcing her to remain trapped against him.

'We can do it easy or we can play rough,' he said calmly into her ear. 'Is that what you like? Do you enjoy being mastered, Luce?'

'Would you try if I said yes?' She spoke into his throat, furiously, the words hissing between her teeth.

His laughter frightened her. 'Yes. I'm always ready for new experiences.'

'New?'

The word was a taunt; it found its target. Luce watched as his lips drew back from his teeth in a smile which was cold and calculating. She wanted to stop this scene, withdraw from it before she got completely out of her depth, but some part of her urged her to stay and fight it out, for if she gave in now Conn would calmly take over her entire life.

'Believe it or not,' he said through lips which barely moved, 'but I've never had to use force to get what I want. Still, if persuasion is your scene—'

His mouth hurt, taking hers with a ferocity that filled her with revulsion. She struggled, but he bent her so far backwards that she lost her balance and fell on to the carpet, her breath knocked from her lungs as he came down on top of her.

One glance at his expression told her that he had intended this humiliation; it was set, fixed in his purpose, and for the first time she felt fear override the excitement engendered by the weight of his body on hers.

'Conn—Please!' The appeal was smothered by his

mouth, forcing hers open in a kiss which revealed his expertise and his intention to hurt. Hot tears sprang to her eyes; she fought viciously, tearing at his shoulders and then at the hand that splayed across one breast, imprisoning it in a hard, painful grip. He laughed deep in his throat, and ripped at the flimsy cotton blouse. The buttons held, but he smiled full into her furious face and increased the pressure. There was a short, tearing sound and she was laid open to his seeking eyes and mouth.

A sob of terror blocked her throat. She knew that he would not be able to dispose of the tough denim of her shorts in so cavalier a manner, and there was no way he could seduce her into removing them voluntarily, so she was safe from the ultimate humiliation. But it was shame enough, the way his mouth explored the soft contours of her breast, that hand moulding the high, small mounds to make a suitable morsel for the savage searching of his lips.

'Stop it,' she moaned, pushing at his face with hands that trembled. 'Conn—please!'

He lifted his head. 'Conn, please,' he mimicked, his glance sweeping contemptuously over the pallor of her face. 'Is this rough enough for you, Luce, or would you like even more?'

Without waiting for an answer he crossed his arms behind her back and lowered himself completely on to her body, pushing her into the coarse warmth of the carpet, the long legs imprisoning hers as he mimicked the thrust of possession. Luce felt she would suffocate, her face pressed into the hardness of his shoulder.

And that was his mistake, for until then he had known exactly what he was doing. Luce heard the indrawn breath which signalled his loss of control and struggled even more violently, afraid now as she had not been before.

'No,' he groaned in an odd voice, and then, on a sigh, 'Dear God, you drive me insane!'

His mouth stopped any response. This time the kiss was gentle, sensuous as he explored the bruised sweetness of her mouth. Luce found herself responding, her hands on his shoulder stilled as the insidious tenderness stormed her defences and levelled them to the ground.

'I could take you here and now,' he said thickly, his lips tracing a path down to the sweep of her shoulder. 'But I won't. I'm too old—I like comfort.'

The wry self-mockery made her smile. 'How old are you?'

'Thirty.' He lifted himself on his elbows, looked down into the quiet surrender of her face, his glance lingering on the sweep of her throat, the soft curves of the breasts his hands and mouth had used so thoroughly. 'You're so beautiful.' The words were gentle, almost awed. 'And I hurt you.'

'Yes. It doesn't matter.'

'It does.' He lifted himself from her, took her hands and bending, hauled her to her feet, keeping her against him. 'Come to Jolie's party, Luce. Please.'

The hand that held the remnants of her blouse across her chest stilled. She looked up at him, met the hard, exciting gaze with wonder and some anger. 'Why?'

He grinned, running his hand up beneath the cotton to cup her breast. 'Because I want you to come,' he said. 'And don't ask me why, or I'll show you. I think we could spend an enjoyable evening together.'

'Ending in some enjoyable activity in a bed, somewhere?'

'Perhaps.' His fingers stroked the smooth skin; he noted her shiver with the eye of a connoisseur. 'But only if you want it. You don't like being over-persuaded, do you?'

'No,' she whispered, and this time the shudder was caused by the memory of those moments when she had thought he might be intending to possess her.

His hands moved to slide across her back and hold her close, his mouth against her forehead. They stood for long moments like this, Luce drawing comfort from his strength and rock-hard steadiness. After a while she sighed, and turned her face against the smooth strength of his throat.

'Do you know what you're doing?' His finger tipped her chin so that he could see her face. 'You're no amateur when it comes to provocation, Luce; it must be inborn. Were you a temptress before you crawled?'

'I don't——' she stopped, aware that to tell him that it was only he on whom she practised her feminine wiles would be revealing too much.

He was right, of course. She seemed impelled to try to force some reaction from him, goading him into the display of violence which had so frightened her, and it had happened again just now when she had almost unconsciously signalled her willingness for further love-making. Conn affected her powerfully, and not only physically, although she knew that if he wanted to woo her into bed with him she would find it extremely difficult to resist. With him, in spite of her resistance to the idea, she found a completeness which satisfied some deep basic hunger in her. The first time she had seen him he had made an ineradicable impression; she had thought it merely that he was a sexually attractive man, but she knew now that it was more than that. He was extremely attractive, possessing a charisma that cast a spell; she had resented that, and until now had refused to admit that his attraction for her was any deeper.

Held now in the comforting clasp of his arms, she forced herself to admit that she was more than halfway to falling in love with him. Superimposed on the basic fact of the physical tension which had sparked between them from the first was an edifice of trust and affection, dependence and need, which frightened her. Surely, she thought wearily, surely time was needed for the development of love; it did not spring into life like a showy, tropical flower—able to survive with neither water nor nourishment. Love needed roots, time to learn about each other, time to grow together.

'Are you certain we don't know each other?' she blurted out, searching the angular features for signs that he was lying to her.

Something flickered beneath the green glaze of his eyes, then vanished. 'Why do you ask?'

'I seem to know you,' she said hopelessly, accepting the fact that his self-control was too great for her to learn anything from his expression.

'Perhaps we've met before in another life.' His voice was light, but his hand smoothed a fine swathe of hair back from her forehead with wonderful gentleness.

Luce gave a choked chuckle. 'I'm having enough trouble with this life to worry about any preceding ones. Although,' with a sweet, mocking glance upwards, 'I can see you as a pirate. Perhaps a buccaneer in Elizabeth's day, tossing off immortal plays in between slitting weazands and looting and raping.'

He frowned, saying with a certain grim impatience, 'You could have stopped that onslaught, but you wanted to provoke me and so you had to take the consequences. Now, write an acceptance for the invitation.'

Before she did so she changed into a dress, choosing one that covered her arms and came high to her throat. She didn't want to take any chances, she told herself; when Conn was being pleasant he was too easy to like.

He lifted an eyebrow at her formality but said nothing. Luce walked across to the table, but before she set pen to notepaper she said quietly, 'Are you sure you want me to go, Conn?'

'I thought I'd made it clear.'

A flush touched her skin. 'Yes, but——' She stopped, staring down at the paper. 'Well, I've no doubt Jolie— oh hell, you know what I mean. If you want an affair, Jolie is half in love with you already, and she knows the rules. I don't. And I don't want an affair, either.'

'I know that.' He smiled at her, looking very sure of

himself. 'My dear girl, you've told me so often enough, and even if you hadn't I'd know. You're a fairly open book in spite of that cool remote air you've cultivated. You don't know very much about men, however. I'm not interested in the Jolie Stewarts of this world. Oh, a few years ago I'd have accepted what she had to offer, but I've learned discrimination since then.' He grinned teasingly at her. 'And celibacy has lost its terrors. So write that acceptance like a good girl and I'll take you out to dinner.'

'Bribery?'

'No, a reward for accepting the inevitable with a good grace.'

So she wrote it, and Conn rang one of the local restaurants, and after leaving a note for Faith they went out. Conn rummaged in the glove box of the car, found a stamp and made her post the acceptance, and then, probably because he had got his own way, showed her just how pleasant and stimulating a companion he could be, so that when Luce came back to the flat she was much more than only half in love with him and the memory of the scene she had provoked was overlaid with others, infinitely more pleasurable.

'A clever man,' she told her reflection as she undressed, her glance brooding on the marks which tomorrow would be bruises. 'And don't you forget it, Luce Laurenson. He eats little girls like you as a snack. And he had absolutely no scruples about the methods he uses to get his own way.'

And she went to bed to weave fantasies which made her blush the next day. Fortunately it was busy, and that evening Sonia rang up and renewed her invitation to stay the weekend of the party with them. Luce accepted.

'Decided to go, after all?'

Her answering smile was weak. 'Yes.'

'Conn persuade you?' Teresa was amused, but her eyes were shrewd as they scanned Luce's averted face.

'You could call it that,' Luce told her drily.

'Well, don't sound so ashamed of it. Few girls would be able to stand up to that one if he really wanted something.'

Luce sighed, staring down at the silvery lilac petals of an African violet with abstracted eyes that saw nothing of the exotic beauty of the plant. Impulsively she asked, 'Teresa, what would you do if you were me?'

'Good heavens, you don't want much, do you!' The older girl considered, frowning slightly. 'If you don't want an affair with him I'd suggest you leave town without a forwarding address. If he attracts you, then just sit back and wait for further developments. If I've judged the man right they won't be long in coming. He's already developed that possessive gleam in his eye when he looks at you which means that he sees you in his bed in the not too distant future.'

'I don't want an affair,' Luce told her quietly—perhaps hoping that if she said it often enough it might become true.

'What do you want?'

'I don't know.' Luce pulled a dying leaf from the pot plant, threw it across the room at the rubbish basket and collapsed into a chair, frowning at her legs. 'I just don't know. I've got this weird feeling that if I—if I do go to bed with him I'll end up crucified.'

'He's made it obvious what he wants?'

A wry smile pulled at the corners of her mouth, 'Oh yes, he's made that quite clear. Jolie is too obvious; I think I intrigue him.'

'It's that remote, touch-me-not look,' Teresa told her wisely. 'But I doubt if he's got marriage in mind, Luce, if that's what you want. I doubt it so much that I'd suggest you put it out of your mind.'

Luce lifted her head, staring at her with an arrested look, as if the suggestion was a monstrous one. 'Do you know,' she said after a long moment, 'do you know, I've never thought of it. Marriage has simply never entered my mind in connection with Conn. Or anyone, if it comes to that. I don't ever see myself as married.'

'I wonder why.' The older girl stirred. 'I've always thought it a natural progression. Not that I viewed every man I went out with as a prospective husband, but surely it's natural to sort of think of those you like in that way. Don't you ever, Luce?'

'No. Never. It's never occurred to me that I'd marry. So you see, I don't think of Conn as suitable husband material.' She smiled ironically. 'Actually, anyone who did would be out of their head. I mean—Conn married! Can you imagine it?'

'Well, he certainly wouldn't be a conventional husband, but I'll bet he'd be a wildly exciting one,' Teresa said, smiling. 'All that arrogance and passion and the hidden hint of violence. Very exciting!'

'You're describing a lover,' Luce told her coolly.

'How about the self-assurance? And that wonderful air of competence? Very desirable for a husband. He's the sort of person who, if you landed up naked on a desert island, would soon have you housed and clothed and a boat well on the way, as well as a horde of dolphins tamed and trained to drive fish into the net.'

Luce laughed at her companion's flight of fancy. 'And still able to take advantage of the tropical moonlight,' she teased.

'Oh that, definitely. He's as sexy as hell and he knows it, and I'll bet he enjoys it. He's as clever as a bag full of monkeys too, and he probably doesn't enjoy that quite so much. Life is not easy for those with a talent, and worse if they've any genius, which Conn may have. But the thing that comes through to me about him, the one way I'd describe him if anyone asked me, is that he has the kind of tough integrity which can be abrasive but is absolutely reliable.'

Luce accepted the truth of the comment with a silence that stretched for long minutes. Not for Conn the easy tactful evasion, the lie to avoid pain; he might refuse to reveal himself, but he would not lie. A complex man, he was not easy to understand, but he did not deliberately set out to dazzle or bewilder. An honest man too, she thought with sardonic weariness, remembering his open avowal of his intentions towards her. Why then could she not accept him as he was, without this continual torment in her brain? For the first time for a long while she pushed her fists into her temples, longing for the memories that lay hidden there. Somewhere there, she was certain now, lay the reasons for her terror at the thought of finding herself at his mercy.

'Is it a matter of principle?' Teresa asked sympathetically.

'I suppose so. Perhaps my mother, whoever she was, kissed me to sleep with the command never to sleep with a man before marriage. No, it's not that, entirely.' Luce pleated her fingers together, frowning at their slender paleness as she searched for words to explain herself. 'It sounds stupid, but it's as if I've been given a post-hypnotic suggestion. I don't have to tell you that I find him attractive.'

'That was obvious right from the start. The air fairly crackled and spat between you. That's why Jolie was so furious.'

'Well, that's how it is. But the thought of being dependent on him for my happiness—and the knowledge that that's what would happen if we became lovers—just fills me with terror.' Luce lifted a pale face to stare across the darkening room at her friend. 'And I mean terror. A sick kind of fear, as though something is eating away inside me. I feel—I feel as though if it happened I'd dwindle into nothing, become a cypher, a zero, a creature without will or thoughts other than his. And I have a horrible feeling that I'm falling in love with him.'

Silence, then Teresa whispered, 'My poor Luce! My dear girl, it sounds as though something is desperately trying to crawl through that barrier in your mind and warn you of something. Do you think—is he a part of your past?'

'He says not, and as you've just said, it's hard to imagine him lying.'

'No, I didn't say that. I said he had integrity. I think he'd lie all right, without turning a hair, if he thought it served a greater truth. Luce, if you don't know him, why should you feel so strongly about him?'

'Oh, perhaps it's just virginal shrinking.' Lifting her hand to her head, Luce summoned up a smile, humourless, but it had the effect of lightening the atmosphere. 'Looked at sensibly, I'm just being hysterical. Perhaps it's the first time I've fallen in love and I'm overwhelmed or something.'

'Perhaps you'd better go to Mattie.'

'Nonsense! She's got better things to do with her time than listen to my ravings.'

Teresa did not try to persuade her, and in the following days Luce grew ashamed of her outburst, especially as Conn didn't come anywhere near her. The season slipped slowly towards summer, the days lengthening into lazy warmth. Luce joined a tennis club and enjoyed herself immensely at the weekends and after work, using the long evenings caused by daylight saving to their full extent. In the effort to win she found a physical exhaustion that made her sleep well at nights. The first Monarch butterflies appeared in the gardens, orange and black beauties with a slow fluttering flight and confiding trustfulness. One settled on Luce's outstretched forefinger, slowly waving its wings as if to cool itself in the soft air.

'Delightful,' Conn said from behind her. 'No doubt rabbits frolic around your toes and birds trill confidingly into your ears.'

Luce's heart leapt in her breast. Not even the sardonic note in the deep voice prevented the smile with which she greeted him.

'Mm, I must stay away some more if that's the response I get when I return,' he drawled, and kissed her, not hard, but taking his time about it as if he had missed her and intended doing something about it.

'I was smiling at the butterfly,' she said, when she could. It was difficult to speak; he had lifted his head but only an inch or so from hers, and his closeness was doing strange things to her. She stepped back, colouring at the mockery of his glance, and held out her hand where the butterfly still reposed.

'Nature girl,' he taunted smoothly, grabbing her hand so that the butterfly, very much on its dignity, rose and made its stately way towards a clump of irises in full flower.

'Why did you do that?'

He grinned. 'Because it cramps my style.' And he kissed her again, only this time there was no holding back. His mouth compelled a response she could not moderate; when he raised his head this time she was pale and breathless and she had felt the convulsive clutch of desire deep within her stomach.

'Yes,' he said, as though she had spoken. 'Come to the beach with me today.'

Caution warred with eagerness within her and her eagerness won. 'O.K. Give me ten minutes.'

He took her to a beach she had never visited before, leaving the road to head across country on a farm track to wind down a bush-covered hill to a cove, small and perfect and pink, where dark red rocks ran out to shelter the water from the swell of the Pacific Ocean. Great pohutukawa trees spread their gnarled limbs over a sandy, grassy area; one branch was already covered with the brilliant scarlet brushes of flowers. A tiny stream tinkled down from the bush-covered hill behind the cove to shimmer across the sand in a sheet of silver. To one side of the cove stood a house, low and dark-stained, the wide windows blind in the vivid sunlight.

Conn drove behind the house, stopped in a garage and switched the engine off.

'Welcome to my retreat,' he said.

'You said we were going to the beach.'

He laughed. 'My child, you can spend the entire day on the beach if you like.'

'Do you live here?'

'Yes.' He grinned and got out of the car, swinging around to open her door. 'I like solitude when I'm working. The homestead is like a three-ring circus most days, so I opted for this.'

'I met your niece the other day,' Luce told him.

'Melissa? Fearsome brat, isn't she? She has her father's strong will and her mother's kind heart.' He pulled her bag from the back of the car and held out a hand to her. 'The boy is Ryan all over again. Not at all kindhearted.'

'Do you think kindness is important?'

That lazy grin eased the hard lines of his features. 'They say that one is attracted to the qualities one doesn't possess. Are you kind, Luce? I don't think I am.'

'No,' she said, half beneath her breath. 'No, you are not kind.'

By now they had walked to the house, into a wide, fresh room which was so windowed that it was barely separated from the magnificent outdoors.

'Then what is it that attracts you?' Conn asked deliberately. 'Cruelty? I've been accused of that.'

A cold shiver brought moisture to her skin. Wide-eyed, she stared up at him, her eyes almost afraid as they traced the magnificent bone structure of his face, the passion revealed by eyes and lips controlled by a fierce self-discipline which must have taken immense effort to acquire.

'No,' she said slowly. 'Cruelty doesn't attract me. It frightens me. You know that.'

'Next you'll tell me that tenderness is what you want, but you'll be lying, Luce. At least partly. You need a master, someone to wring the responses from you that you refuse to give freely.' He touched her shoulder, his hand slipping across the smooth golden skin to rest at the nape of her neck. Very gently, as though afraid that she would flinch away, his fingers explored the hollow behind an ear, moving with such sensuous appreciation that she shuddered, biting her lip to prevent herself from revealing just how his touch affected her.

'You see,' he said quietly, 'you're resisting me now.'

'I must be a very common type,' she said thickly. 'You don't know me very well, yet you've already pinned me out on a board and labelled me.'

Conn smiled, the green depths of his eyes dark, hiding whatever reaction he had to her words.

'No, I rather think you are unique,' he returned.

'Then it must be all that experience the gossip columnists make such a play of which enables you to classify me so quickly and accurately.' Luce hadn't intended the words to sound so bitter, and bit her lip with chagrin when he laughed softly and pulled her towards him.

'Gossip columnists are truly creative,' he told her coolly, his mouth only inches from hers. 'What they don't know they make up. Are you adopting a high moral tone, or is it the idea of me, specifically, gaining experience which makes you so disdainful?'

He lowered his head and kissed the corner of her mouth, the warm firmness of him calling up a host of sensations that seemed to scramble her thoughts into hopeless confusion. She discovered that she wanted him to kiss her properly, she wanted to stand breast to breast and hip to hip, sealed together in an embrace. A flush heated her skin as she owned to herself that what she really wanted was to lie in his arms and discover what it was like to feel him invade her body and take possession of it.

'When you want to go to bed with me your eyes go heavy, like thunderclouds in a grey sky,' he commented, and watched with a sardonic eye as her colour deepened and she lowered her lashes, her lips suddenly dry.

'How about you?' she said, stupidly, too shocked by

the erotic images her sensitised nerves were conjuring up to be sensible of what she was saying.

He laughed, and put his hands on her hips, holding her closely but not too hard against him so that she could feel how aroused he was. 'As you see,' he taunted softly, and made no effort to hold her when she stepped back. 'Don't look so harassed, Luce, I've no intention of seducing you today. At least, not unless you signify that you want it as much as I do. And that you're not going to regret it afterwards.'

'I suppose I must seem an idiot to you,' she said, turning away to unpack the contents of the hamper she had brought.

'No. Why should you think that?' When she didn't answer he grinned and pulled a soft strand of her hair. 'I think you're young and inexperienced, and that although your memories of the past are gone, whatever trauma caused your amnesia has carried over into your present life, making you wary and super-cautious. And as I am not, contrary to your very obvious opinion, only interested in going to bed with women, I'm more than happy to spend a very pleasant day with you with only a minor amount of lovemaking. O.K.?'

'O.K.,' she agreed, not entirely trustful even yet, but with her fears eased by his frankness.

'So. A swim first, I think, to work up an appetite for lunch.'

'O.K.' Impelled by a yearning she recognised only too well, Luce watched as he moved away to pull his shirt over his head.

A cry broke from between her lips.

'What the hell——?' Startled, he looked up, his expression hardening as he took in the dilated eyes and trembling mouth. 'What on earth's the matter?'

'Your shoulder!' Luce put out her hand, her fingers touching the short thick scar that marred the dark skin. 'Conn, where—how did you get that appalling scar?'

He stood very still, lids lowered to hide any expression

in his eyes. There was an intent waiting quality to the silence that stretched between them as her forefinger stroked the ugly puckered tissue. Luce felt a horror out of all proportion to the mark; it was stupid, an over-reaction so violent that her head began to ache with the intensity of her emotions.

Without thinking she kissed the scar, forcing back tears. Conn's arm came to rest across her shoulders. She could feel the tension in him, the taut muscles, the watchful silence.

'How did you get it?' she repeated, afraid of that silence.

'In a car accident.'

Her head throbbed. 'I'm sorry,' she said harshly. 'I must be going mad.'

'It's not a pleasant sight.' He turned her chin so that she met the hard scrutiny of his gaze. 'Relax, Luce. It's all right. It happened a couple of years ago and I'm well over it now.'

Perhaps he waited for an answer. She could say nothing, but after a moment she nodded, relaxing against him.

It took half an hour for the headache to go away and after that it was a very pleasant day, a jewel of a day, in a setting of enamelled blue sky and sea, sand that glittered like powdered diamonds and the soft, sensual hush of the sea on the shore. They swam and sunbathed, explored the immediate environs of the bay and ate lunch in the shade of the pohutukawa trees. After that, replete with food and half of the bottle of white wine which Conn produced from the fridge, Luce slept, her head pillowed in her arms.

She awoke to a sensation of such security and warmth that for long moments she lay with her eyes closed, refusing to analyse the source of such an unusual feeling. Only slowly it became apparent that it was because she was lying enclosed in Conn's arms, one beneath her neck, the other heavy across her waist and down her thigh, the fingers splayed out gently on the skin above her knee. She could feel the rise and fall of his chest against her back, the hair-roughened strength of his legs against hers. His chin rested on the top of her head. And she knew that she loved him, totally, irrevocably, without beginning or end.

And that she could not permit him to become her lover, because if she did he would take not only her heart with him when he left, but all that made her life worth living.

She should have felt despair, but joy sang through her veins and a smile curved her lips. Out at sea a gull called, distance lending false enchantment to its cry; the regular, steady beat of his heart almost drowned it out. He moved and the hand on her leg came up and rested against her breast, a moment before slackening into the looser grip of deep sleep. She smiled again and sighed a little. At least she had these minutes with him, free from the confusion of desire.

Too soon he stirred, muttered something, then said quite clearly, 'Darling . . .' He woke instantly, like an animal when it is threatened, and for a moment froze. Then his hand touched her heart and he said with laughter deep in his voice, 'How long have you been awake?'

'Not long.' Luce turned, determined to keep things light.

Conn was smiling, the planes and angles of his face still relaxed in the aftermath of sleep. From beneath those heavy lids his eyes gleamed as they roamed her face; for a moment she thought she detected a sharp indrawn breath, but he bent as if to hide himself from too probing a gaze and bit the lobe of her ear.

'You're nice to wake up to,' he murmured lazily, laughter in his voice.

'So are you. Conn, was Jolie telling the truth when she said that you asked her to dinner at your sister's place and she couldn't go?'

He was very still, then pulled her against him, so that she could feel the latent strength in him, and said with calm amusement, 'No, my inquisitive delight, she wasn't. To start with, it was Sonia who invited you. I may have moments of boorishness, but I don't invite strangers to Sonia's house without making sure she's quite happy about it. And although Sonia is a dear, she loves her husband devotedly and studies his wishes. Ryan doesn't like Jolie. Her parents, yes, but not their regrettably forward daughter. So Sonia would need a fair amount of coaxing to have Jolie to dinner.' He laughed. 'It's only fair to add that the feeling is entirely mutual. Only Jolie is frightened of Ryan.'

'Oh, so am I,' Luce said fervently.

'Really? He's a tough character, but as Sonia likes you he'll not eat you. Anyway, you have me to defend you.'

'I'm frightened of you, too. You're two of a kind.'

His chest lifted with his laughter. 'Is this how you normally signal your fear? You feel very much at home in my arms, Luce, as if you belong there. Wouldn't you like to?'

'For how long?'

'Does it matter?'

He held her firmly against him. After lying in the sun Luce had put her blouse back on, but Conn, accustomed, as he told her, to a paler sun, had remained dressed only in the battered pair of denim shorts which he had donned after his swim. Now there seemed to be too much of him, too much tanned skin with its faint, evocative scent, too much tangle of hair across his chest and on the legs, one of which now held hers imprisoned.

Luce's heart stopped, then began to race. 'You said you wouldn't,' she began. 'Conn, *please*!'

'Does it matter how long I stay as your lover?'

There was enough hard insistence in his voice to make her lift her head from its resting place on the wall of his chest. 'Yes,' she said defiantly.

'Why?'

She flushed but held his glance. 'You know why. I've told you I'm not geared to casual love affairs.'

Something gleamed beneath his lashes. 'What do you mean by casual?'

'Just that.' She tried to pull away, but he refused to loosen his hold. 'Conn, don't be a beast! Why won't you believe that I don't want to become your mistress?'

'Because when we lie like this that pulse in your throat beats like a terrified bird. Your lips refuse me, but body language is a different thing and whatever you say, however hard you try to convince me otherwise, you'd like it very much if I overruled your objections and took you without giving you any options.'

Shamed colour flooded her cheeks and throat and she turned her head away so that he couldn't see how accurate his assessment of the situation was. 'You're hateful,' she muttered furiously.

His chuckle stirred the fine fronds of hair across the top of her head. 'I know. But I'm not going to seduce you, Luce. When you come to me you'll come because you want it, because you've finally convinced that brain of yours that you needn't fear me. Then . . .' His voice roughened as he moved, rolling her on to her back to hold her pinned against the rug by her shoulders, his hands hurtful against the smooth taut skin. 'Then, Luce, I'll show you what it's like to lose your mind completely. I'm going to make you forget that you're anything but a collection of sensations and needs and desires that will eat you up if they're not satisfied.'

The hard passion in his voice forced an answering hunger deep inside her. To shut out the sight of his handsome, tough features she closed her eyes, but that was even worse, for he began to kiss her, softly at first while his hands cradled her face, and then, when she relaxed and parted her lips for him, more and more deeply until she began to shake with the need to feel him on her and within her.

'And you'd better believe it,' he said, a thin thread of amusement in the deep tones as he spoke against her lips.

Luce forced herself to acquire some control, deliberately relaxing muscles racked by an intolerable hunger, breathing slowly and regularly until she felt courageous enough to open her eyes. Through lips swollen by the demanding pressure of his she said defiantly, 'I've heard and read often enough—that the first time is not much fun for a woman. And that it takes a tender and considerate lover to help her reach any great heights.'

Conn grinned, and kissed her nose, sliding his hand beneath her blouse to find the tip of her breast. Lucy flinched as his fingers encircled it, giving rise to a needle of desire which turned to a surge as he followed his hand with his lips.

'Are you implying that I'm not tender or considerate?' he asked mockingly, and then released her so that she was assailed by a sensation of cold and rejection. 'Well, my Lady Disdain, you'll just have to wait and see.'

And for the rest of the afternoon he was infuriatingly friendly, treating her as though she was an intelligent but sexless companion. Luce found herself first perplexed, then angry, mostly with herself for being so easily manipulated. That he knew exactly what he was doing was made clear when he kissed her at the door of the flat—a chaste salute on her cheek—and whispered, 'I'll wait until you're ready.'

Anger forced a shrug, but he had her, and he kne it. Somehow he had become necessary to her, as necessary as food and sunlight, so basic a part of her life that when he went it would be like losing a limb

CHAPTER SIX

JOLIE was lucky with the weather for her coming of age. It had been a week of languorous days smiled upon by a tender sky, warmed by a beneficent sun. Already farmers were talking with cautious optimism about one of those years that made other seasons of drought and wind and disease worthwhile. There had been enough rain to keep the grass growing, but not so much as to engender a facial eczema scare; the hay stood tall and silver in the paddocks. Home gardeners watched proudly as tomato, sweetcorn and green pepper plants grew enthusiastically. On fruit trees the tiny green globes of peaches and plums and apples expanded and over the orchards lay the heavy perfume of citrus flowers.

'I believe the Stewart place is like something out of *House and Garden*,' said Faith as she folded the black chiffon confection Luce was to wear that night.

'Then I'll prefer the McLeod homestead,' Luce muttered. 'It's beautiful, but it looks like a home.'

She was nervous, tension pulling at her until she had to sit down on the side of her bed and take several deep breaths.

'Relax.' Faith laid the gown into the small suitcase Teresa had lent. 'You know, you've gone all eyes just lately. Is Conn giving you a hard time?'

'Far from it.' Luce reflected gloomily that it would have been easier to deal with someone who kept steering her towards the nearest bed. But Conn hadn't given so much as a glance towards a bed; for these past few weeks he had been almost unnaturally circumspect. Like a beast of prey with all the time in the world he stalked her, keeping his desires far enough out of sight in the hope that she would relax her guard. He made it quite

106

obvious that any move to a closer relationship was going to have to come from her, and the tension of subduing the painful love she felt was wearing at her nerves.

Restlessly she moved to avoid her friend's too shrewd glance. 'No, he's been very—very noncommittal,' she said, slipping sandals into a plastic bag.

'Not losing interest, however.' Faith sat on the small chair. 'He's hunting. I'll bet he was born knowing all the tricks.' She hesitated, then said quietly, 'Have you ever wondered whether he might be married, Luce?'

'No.' After a moment Luce repeated, 'No, I've not. We—surely we'd have known? I mean—gossip columnists and such?'

She was talking for the sake of talking, giving herself time to come to terms with the idea.

'Perhaps, but it's the sort of thing that might have easily been overlooked. I'm probably wrong, mind you, but I don't suppose in the circles he moves in it would make overmuch difference. I mean, they seem to swap spouses with charming lightheartedness, don't they, every other year or so.'

'Somehow I can't imagine Conn being quite so broadminded,' Luce remarked drily. 'He's the possessive type. I rather suspect that any wife he married would stay firmly attached or he'd want to know the reason why.'

'I rather suspect you're right.' Faith was thoughtful, her broad brow wrinkled slightly. 'You know him well, don't you?'

'What parts of him he reveals, yes, I suppose I do. But he's not the easiest of people to understand.'

'No, and yet you seem to go together. I mean, you fit together.' Faith laughed somewhat selfconsciously. 'I know exactly what I mean, but it's a bit difficult to express. You dovetail, like two people who've been happily married for some years. You complement each other. And you call him possessive. It's as though you're linked by a terrifically strong bond, which is quite ridiculous, because you've only known each other a couple of months and it was there on that first meeting.'

'Physical attraction.'

'That too, but it's more than that.' Faith grinned, self-mocking. 'If I wanted to be old-fashioned I'd say you were almost like soulmates. And I can just imagine Conn's derision at such a description.'

'Oh, so can I.' Luce began to poke in a few small things that were left, glad to be bending so that Faith couldn't see her face. 'You like him, don't you?'

'Yes, I like him. Immensely. He's an absorbingly fascinating creature. He reminds me of a tiger at the zoo, beautiful and lazy and good-humoured as it stretches out along a log, but you know that beneath that sleepy exterior there's a cold brain and a ferocity which is barely hidden. If you weren't so level-headed I'd worry about you.'

Luce laughed, pretending to believe her, and knew that both Faith and Teresa were concerned about the relationship. Anger tightened her lips as she remembered Conn's scathing comments about them and their attitude towards her. It was easy enough for him, she thought; for herself she could never be thankful enough for their undemanding affection these past two years.

Soon afterwards Conn arrived to take her to the McLeods' homestead. As always he was charm itself to Faith and Teresa, but when the car pulled away he slanted her a glance, saying, 'How have I offended you this time?'

'Not at all,' she said stiffly, irritated by his perception.

'Then relax.' He picked up her hand and held it beneath his for a moment on the wheel. 'Sonia is looking forward to having you to stay.'

'How about Ryan?'

He chuckled. 'Ryan wants Sonia to have whatever she wants, so yes, he's looking forward to it too.'

'If that's meant to be reassuring I've missed out on

something,' she muttered.

His soft laughter seemed to fill the car. Luce removed her hand from beneath his and stared with determination out of the window. After a while the gentle sweep of the countryside restored her good humour. She waved to two children riding bareback on a draught horse, watched with irritated amusement as Conn eyed with considerable speculation a glorious bikini-clad creature who was mowing the grass verge, and found herself coaxed into reluctant laughter as he slid a teasing glance her way.

'That's better,' he said. 'For a minute there I thought you were going to do something drastic.'

'I don't care if your eyes fall out watching bikini girls,' she said, half laughing, half angry.

'No?' His hand closed over hers in a grip that tightened painfully for a second. 'I'm nowhere near as complaisant, I'm afraid. Remember tonight that you are my partner.'

'Jealousy?'

'You'd better believe it.'

The words were softly spoken, but there was no doubt they were a warning. Luce looked across at a profile hard as that of a stone statue and felt a cold clutch of fear mixed with the anguish of unsatisfied desire in the pit of her stomach.

'So remember,' he told her calmly, 'you're mine.'

He took too much for granted. 'Your partner,' she returned with the faintest hint of a snap in the words.

'If it makes you feel happier.'

It didn't, but Luce forbore to press the point. There was an angularity about his features that warned her that he was keeping some strong emotion in check and that it would not take much to loose it. She began to talk of an incident in the shop yesterday, using her seldom invoked talent for mimicry to make him smile and then laugh, and the tension in him eased.

'Are you being feminine and devious?' he asked, and

when she nodded he grinned and picked up her hand, but this time it was pressed to his mouth. 'Clever Luce!'

His long finger touched the wild flurry of her pulse, and then he set her hand back in her lap, saying oddly, 'I wish—sometimes I wish that life could reverse itself.'

'It would make an interesting play.'

'I'm sure it's been done before. Certainly it has in science fiction. I've read a book about a man who's sent back to relive his life, after being told that he'll repeat every action he regrets in the first life. He has his memory, but finds that he's forced by the situations he finds himself in into exactly the same mistakes.'

Luce shivered. 'I'd hate to think that was possible.'

'I think it's probably correct,' he said. 'Free will is just an illusion. You don't really want to be here with me, do you, heading out to a weekend with people you hardly know, going to the birthday party of a girl you actively dislike?'

The harsh cynicism in his voice made her flinch. 'No, I don't. In fact, I'm damned if I know what I'm doing here.'

'You're here because I persuaded you to come, using methods hardly according to Hoyle. And because there's something, some bond between us that you can't free yourself from.'

Shaken both by the flat conviction of his voice and his echoes of Faith's remark, she asked, 'What about you? What would you rather be doing?'

'My dear girl, need you ask?' He slanted a wickedly taunting glance at her profile, watching as embarrassment washed over her skin in a flood of colour. 'I'd like to be with you in a large bed in a small house, a hundred miles away from the nearest person, with several months of solitude before us——'

He continued speaking, but Luce shut out the words, holding her hands over her ears until he laughed, and said loudly, 'Prude! And if you want to spare yourself blushes, don't ask leading questions.'

Luce leaned forward and switched the radio on, unable to look anywhere but at her hands. One of these fine days she just might learn to guard her impetuous tongue!

Fortunately he said nothing more, concentrating instead on taking the car smoothly around the series of sharp corners that marked the stretch of road just before the McLeods' station.

And then they were there, and there was no time for any further conversation as Luce met once again the redoubtable Melissa and was introduced to her brother, a quieter, more reserved child with his father's straight, clear glance.

Ryan was out working on the station; he came in while they were having afternoon tea on a wide flagstoned terrace overlooking the swimming pool. He was charming, Sonia was her usual sweet self, even Conn seemed more relaxed than Luce had ever seen him. Insensibly she too began to relax, and by the time it came to change for dinner she was even beginning to look forward to the party a little.

Certainly, she decided as she viewed herself in the mirror, she looked well. Sunbathing had given her a delicate golden glow which was enhanced by the soft dark chiffon of her dress. And that was so demure as to be daring, the full sleeves falling to her elbows, the neckline revealing entrancing glimpses of smooth skin. With it she wore only earrings, pale moonstones which fell from her ears to brush her neck, and a spray of 'Chloe' perfume, a heavy tuberose scent which should have cloyed but suited her mood tonight.

In the mirror her eyes sparkled, mysterious, a little fey, as pale as the moonstones that rested against the long lovely curve of her neck. The only touch of colour was her mouth, as full and passionate as her eyes were remote.

When she walked into Conn's presence she watched as he looked up, and saw for a moment naked desire, and then pain when he saw her. It was as if her beauty stirred him to the depths but brought only despair with it. His words echoed her intuition.

'La Belle Dame Sans Merci,' he said softly, for her ears alone.

'Is that what I am? The personification of lust divorced from love?'

He smiled, completely master of himself once more. 'Is that what that poem is about? Come and have a drink before we go.'

They travelled separately to the Stewarts' homestead, only a few miles along the road. Luce felt a return of her former unease, or perhaps, she thought wryly, an intensification of the foreboding which had never left her. The evening was mild and clear, cool enough to make dancing pleasant, warm enough to make outdoor activities equally attractive. Everything combined for a wonderful evening. Luce knew that she looked superb, slid a sideways glance at her companion and met his undeniably possessive regard. Tonight she would be envied by every unattached woman there and probably by many of the married ones. And yet a sensation of doom was pinning her back into the seat and she felt a reluctance so strong as to be fear.

'Conn——' Her voice trailed away.

'What is it?'

'I don't want to go.'

He frowned. 'We've been through that. You're going. Of course . . .' his eyes gleamed suddenly, 'if you made it worthwhile I might turn back to my place.'

Luce bit her lip. 'No, thanks,' she said icily.

'That's the only choice you have.'

'You're a beast! Sometimes I think you hate me.'

'I don't hate you.' His profile was etched hard against the pale pink of the evening sky. 'I despise myself for wanting you and I resent you, but I don't hate you. It would be different if you'd set out to capture me, but you didn't, did you?'

'No.' She wasn't surprised by his brutal honesty, nor was she hurt. His emotions were too much like her own; resentment at the strength of the physical ties that bound them, self-contempt at her weakness in being unable to break free of them. 'Why does it happen this way?'

'Who knows? Desire is the wild card in the pack. The only way to break its chains is to give in to it, to become sated and at last sickened. But you won't do that.'

'I'd rather die,' she said harshly, chilled and appalled at the pictures his savage, bitter voice conjured up.

'Is that just the conventional reaction of the virgin confronted by some of the less pleasant facts of life? Or do you really feel that to become my lover would be a kind of death for you?'

'I told you once that it would,' she replied tonelessly, staring out of the windscreen at the smooth, opulent countryside around them. 'It would be like walking into a furnace.'

'Nevertheless, you'll do it.' As she flinched Conn said with quiet emphasis, 'I don't want emotional commitment; I don't care if you hate my guts. All I want is the feel of you in my arms and the sound of you as you find out just how pleasurable physical love can be.'

Something kicked in her stomach, a hot, debilitating tide of desire conjured up by his words and the erotic images they evoked. Luce closed her hands, forcing her nails into the soft palms until the pain brought her back to her senses.

'I've no doubt that lovemaking would be wonderful,' she said, her voice hard. 'It's the aftermath that worries me.'

They had turned off the road between two large old pillars of volcanic stone, now overgrown with ivy. The drive was dark beneath puriri and karaka trees. As they swung into a wide gravelled area Conn said coolly:

'We'll continue this fascinating conversation later on.'

'Why don't you go back home and leave me alone?'

'Because you're like a disease. You have to run your course before I'm free of you, and you haven't got beyond being a fever in my blood yet.' He stopped the car, turned so that he could see where he intended to reverse to and continued, 'And I'm going to take you through every stage, my dear, until we both of us reach convalescence and eventually full recovery. Regardless of your fears and fancies.'

The hard decision of his voice made her shiver, but she retorted with spirit, 'Thanks for warning me. I'll make sure I'm not alone with you ever again!'

He grinned, stopped the car and ran his fingers lightly up her arm beneath the soft fold of chiffon to her shoulder. A wild floodtide of sensation followed the gentle movement of his fingertips; she heard her breath hiss in between her lips and said deep in her throat, 'Don't, Conn . . .'

'You're beautiful,' he murmured, leaning forward so that his breath touched her forehead. 'And you remind me very much of Helen of Troy. Just don't forget who you came with.'

'You're very classical and poetic tonight! First La Belle Dame, and now Helen of Troy.'

He smiled again, tilted her chin and kissed the corner of her mouth, 'Ah, but they were both the same woman, weren't they?'

'Then how about this?' It was hard to think with his mouth resting lightly against her skin and his hand smoothing the soft flesh of her shoulder, but from deep in her subconscious she summoned up the excoriating lines of one of Shakespeare's sonnets:

> 'The expense of spirit in a waste of shame
> Is lust in action; and till action, lust
> Is perjured . . .'

Her voice trembled, but she continued:

> 'Enjoyed no sooner but despised straight;

Past reason hunted; and no sooner had,
Past reason hated . . .'

Silence stretched between them, long and filled with
tension and pain.

'Isn't that what you're summoning?' she said quietly.

'Shakespeare was a superb poet. The sonnets are an
exercise in self-indulgence, an exorcising of emotions he
couldn't handle any other way. He couldn't resist the
temptation to dramatise everything.' The words were
cool, dismissive, spoken against her cheek so that she
forgot the anguish and responded with an involuntary
movement of her body that brought her closer to him.

'Just as you do,' Conn taunted, and leaned over to
unlock the door.

Luce could have screamed with frustration. He knew
her weakness and used it to his own advantage, stripping
away the armour she so carefully built around herself
until she was forced to fight him with her pitifully weak
weapons. Always, always it was he who called the tune,
who decided when to kiss and when to stop, when to
tease and when to be serious. If just once she could see
him at a disadvantage she almost thought she could die
happily.

Jolie looked superb in a slinky dress of green that
displayed her figure splendidly, as well as the emeralds
she had coveted. She greeted Luce with an effusiveness
which was patently false, allowed her glance to linger
hungrily on Conn's dark features for just too long, then
escorted them into a room which was already well filled
with people.

It was the first big party Luce had been to since she
found herself with no memory, yet it followed so
familiar a pattern that she knew she had experienced
such occasions often before.

Which was odd, she thought. Surely most eighteen-
year-olds didn't lead such very social lives?

Everyone was very friendly. Conn, of course, was the

celebrity, but even had no one known of his fame he would have drawn all eyes. He had that air of effortless authority enhanced by the kind of magnetism which is only partly sexual. It was a bedrock self-confidence, she decided. Reduced to its simplest and most basic terms Conn was a survivor, the sort of man one could trust in a situation where life was at stake. Ryan was another such, and there were two other men in the room who had that aura, but none of them possessed the personal charisma or the hard good looks which made Conn stand out in any crowd, even one of wealthy New Zealanders such as this.

Some may have been faintly patronising at the thought of an English dramatist; it took only one look at him for them to realise their mistake. He won an instant respect because he was the man he was. And while the men found him interesting their womenfolk were fascinated by his dark charm.

He responded, of course, but there was no doubt as to who his partner was. Some primitive part of Luce enjoyed the total possession of his attitude towards her, but it also irritated her.

When asked to dance by a young man who had been eyeing her for some moments she was ready to accept. But Conn slid an arm about her waist and said, 'No.' And his eyes said, without embarrassment, she's mine, and if you know what's good for you you'll get the hell out of here.

Which the brash young man did, his speed revealing just how much Conn's hard stare had affected him.

Luce was furious, but the pressure of his fingers against her narrow waist warned her not to speak and she had to content herself with an angry sparkling glance from beneath her lashes which was met with a blandness all the more infuriating for being tinctured with laughter. Conn resumed his conversation, and after a few minutes she relaxed enough to join in.

And then he took the glass from her fingers, put it

with his on a convenient table, excused them and drew
her into the big tiled playroom which was where the
group played, and without a word slipped his arm
around her waist and began to dance.

'Still angry?'

Luce bit her lip, only too conscious of the insidious
sensuality of the music and his closeness. 'A bit. Did
you have to be quite so brutal?'

'Yes.' His arm tightened, forcing her against him. 'He
was poaching and he knew it.'

'And don't my wishes have anything to do with it?'

'Did you want to dance with him?'

'Oh, go to hell!' she retorted explosively, reacting to
the taunt in his voice. 'Arrogant bastard!'

'Shh, someone might hear you.'

He was laughing at her, the narrowed green of his
eyes mocking her inability to resist him. Suddenly a pang
of fear and anguish shot through her; she stared up at
him, her mouth a crimson flower against the pallor of
her skin.

'What is it?' he asked harshly, stopping. 'What's the
matter?'

'I don't—I don't know.' She stared around, her expression hunted. 'Conn, I want to go home.'

'No.'

When she moaned he steered her through the wide
doors on to a terrace and stood, his back to the lights
so that she was sheltered from any curious glances.

'Oh—Conn . . .' Almost she begged, her voice trembling. Waves of nausea were submerging her, and a
half-remembered agony that made breathing almost
impossible.

'Relax,' he ordered, deep tones softening the command. 'Don't try to remember, darling, just let it go. It
will come, when the time is right.'

Luce began to shudder, her eyes bleached of all colour
in the dim light, the only colour the dark lashes and
brows that outlined them. The nausea passed, leaving

her weak; she found that he was holding her hands and with a quiet sob she swayed against him, taking comfort from his strength.

He held her for long moments until her body stilled and colour began to tinge the damp skin of her face.

'I wonder if they'll think me an alcoholic if I ask for a neat brandy,' he said into her ear. 'I'll have to risk it. With any luck they'll think it an idiosyncrasy of genius.'

She smiled, as he meant her to, and sat on the seat nearby. As long as he was in sight her eyes dwelt on him, then she looked with a blank lack of interest at the scene before her.

It was almost an enchantment. Between two wings of the house the Stewarts had built a swimming pool, now lit from beneath the water; several young boys were swimming, their shouts clear above the music of the band. Around the pool was a wide area of split sandstone, the silver slabs of stone outlined by honey-scented ribbons of alyssum, pink, white, purple and lilac. There were shrubs in pots and trees like the one she sat beneath had been planted between the flagstones. People talked and laughed in groups beneath the fairy lights, the women exquisitely gowned against the sombre formality of the men. Jolie had no reason to doubt the success of her party. It had all the ingredients of a superb affair.

Luce sat, a tense, withdrawn figure, wondering why she should have been so affected by Conn's taunt. If she knew that, of course, she would no longer have amnesia.

She had been watching Jolie for some time before she realised who she was, and it was some seconds more before she realised that her hostess was making her way towards her.

'Oh *no*,' she muttered beneath her breath, but she was now too limp with reaction to make her escape. She could only hope that Conn would come and rescue her soon. And the knowledge that she was so dependent on him made her feel sick again.

'Feeling the heat?' Jolie's voice was falsely pleasant, for even in the dimness Luce could see the twisted smile bestowed on her.

'Just a little.'

'I'd have thought you'd have got used to our summers by now.' Jolie sat down beside Luce, her hand touching the emeralds at her ears. Without pausing she continued, 'Did you know that Conn is married?'

After the conversation with Faith it seemed like an incredible coincidence that Jolie should throw this at her. She hadn't believed it before and she didn't believe it now.

'No,' she said in a polite little voice that made the older woman stiffen.

'Well, he is. He married some very well-connected woman in London a couple of years ago.' Goaded into further revelations by the complete lack of interest in Luce's profile she added spitefully, 'I didn't think he'd told you. As soon as I knew . . .'

The innuendo was clear. As soon as I knew he was married I dropped him.

She was lying, of course. She was still violently attracted to him, and if he crooked his finger Jolie would be at his side, wife or no wife.

For herself Luce didn't believe in any wife, but she said, 'Who told you about it?'

'Oh, apparently it's fairly well known in theatrical circles. My aunt is friends with an actress in Auckland who knows him and she told her.' The smooth voice became heavy with sympathy as Jolie leaned towards her. 'I'm sorry if it's a shock, but I felt I should tell you before you got in too deep.'

Conn was making his way towards them, a glass in his hand. Luce watched him, her heart contracting into a tight hard ball in her chest. As he came up behind Jolie she said, lifting her voice a little, 'Why, Conn, Jolie has just told me something rather startling about you.'

She heard the other woman's hissing breath, then Jolie

was twisting away from her, her expression tormented as she babbled, 'Con—I——'

'Indeed?' He handed the glass to Luce and said quietly, 'Drink up, Luce.' Then the dark intent glance moved to Jolie, holding her still against the pale trunk of the tree. 'Telling tales, Jolie?' he asked.

Luce was frightened and ashamed of herself. Jolie had intended to hurt her, but she was behaving just as badly. A cat fight, she thought distastefully, and over a man!

'Leave it,' she said now, trying to regain the initiative.

The other two ignored her. 'Jolie?' Conn asked softly, his expression completely impassive, yet there was such menace in that one word that Luce was not surprised when Jolie began to tremble.

Her mouth worked silently: for a moment defiance lit the dark eyes and then faded and she looked at him with an expression of such blind subjugation that Luce's nausea returned in full measure.

'I told her that you're married,' Jolie said thinly. 'I'm sorry, Conn. I didn't—I wanted——' She put out her hand to touch his and then whispered, 'I'm sorry,' again before running across the terrace towards the house.

Very carefully Luce put the glass down on the seat; as she swayed and fell she was caught by arms strong enough to hold her close against a driving irregularly beating heart.

CHAPTER SEVEN

IT was three o'clock in the morning before she got to bed, but although she was exhusted she lay for long hours in the luxurious bedroom and watched the slow wheel of the stars past her window.

Incredibly her faint had gone unnoticed. When she recovered consciousness she was still clasped in Conn's arms. He had sat her down, insisted on her sipping the brandy, and after a few minutes her head had cleared and the warmth of the spirit had given her enough strength to follow his lead. And his lead was to ignore the whole sordid little incident. Incredibly enough, it worked. He never left her side but rarely spoke directly to her; the only time they separated was when she danced with Ryan, and even then Conn was waiting for her, his hand ready to take hers, so that by the end of the evening everyone there must have decided that she and Conn were on the brink of an affair, if not in the throes of one.

Bewildered by his calm attitude, Luce had managed to adopt it for her own. To her considerable surprise she found that she almost enjoyed the evening. Jolie had stayed away from them, their only contact with her being as they said their farewells and then the sherry-coloured eyes had avoided Conn's and Jolie's voice had had a shrill undertone which made Luce uneasy.

She felt profoundly sorry for the girl. There was a kind of sick despair in Jolie's eyes which was frightening. Jolie had made the mistake of allowing herself to be ensnared by a sexuality of such dark power that she had been unable to resist it. On the way back to the homestead Luce told herself that she too had become a prisoner, trapped by an aura of magnetism and the rock-hard impregnability of the man.

Not the same way as Jolie, she decided now. Jolie wanted him, and her hunger was a thing by itself, divorced from the woman, almost divorced from the man. It wasn't Conn she needed so much as the sensations she knew he could arouse in her.

Whereas she. . . . Luce smiled sadly, pushing a wave of hair back from her forehead in a weary gesture. Had she fallen in love with him? If love was this aching need, this yearning to give and give and give, to spend oneself in a prodigality of emotion, then yes, she was in love with him. It seemed to have sprung to life full-blown in that first moment of seeing at Waipu Cove, and although she had been in retreat ever since she had known that sooner or later she would be forced to face the truth.

The curtains lifted and billowed in a vagrant breeze which brought in all of the odours of a summer night, the sweet perfumes from Sonia's garden, the fresh evocative scent of a newly mown lawn and over all a faint tang of salt, for the sea was not far away across the hills. Wide-eyed, Luce tried to sort her emotions into recognisable bundles, but was baffled by the deep melancholy which held her in its grip. If only· love brought happiness in its train!

She got up and walked across to the window, drawn by desires older than time. Dawn was not far away. Already the sky to the east had lightened, but although a lamb bleated it was still too early for the dawn chorus of birds. Luce stood for a long moment watching as the dark figure of a man walked beneath a pergola starred with jasmine flowers. Even foreshortened there was no mistaking him. Conn too was unable to sleep, driven by who knew what devils to walk off his restlessness in the warm erotic night.

What was he thinking of as he paced the length of the pergola?

Luce turned swiftly back into the room and got into

bed. He had not mentioned Jolie's accusation and neither had she, but now the questions came like ants around sugar, bedevilling her. All she had was her own deep-rooted conviction that he was single to set against Jolie's confident assertion. And the days when intuition could be trusted were long past.

But surely Sonia would have said something? His own sister would know whether he was married. It hurt to think that she cared so little about Luce that she had not even warned her. Assuming that it was true, and not just a vicious item of gossip.

Incredibly Luce slept. When she woke it was almost lunchtime and Sonia was laughing in the kitchen with her children, her clear gaze amused when Luce opened the door.

'My dear, you look so fresh!' she exclaimed. 'The coffee's perking. Would you like some?'

'I'm conscience-stricken,' said Luce, accepting a cup gratefully. 'You should have woken me up.'

Sonia chuckled. 'Ryan got up at eight and took the kids with him while he did his rounds, the darling, so I slept in till ten.'

'And Conn?'

Something flashed into the green eyes so like her brother's, then as quickly disappeared. 'Oh, he took off about nine o'clock, but he's back now. I think he wants to take you to the beach this afternoon.'

'Oh?' Luce looked annoyed. 'Charming soul, isn't he? One of these days he might think to ask me if I want to do these things.'

'It's a waste of time.' He came in through the back door, throwing Luce a look which was at once a challenge and a statement of intent. 'You're coming.' And when she didn't answer he said softly, 'Aren't you?'

Their eyes met, clashed and disengaged, leaving Luce shaken. Clearly he had come to some decision during the night and he had no intention of letting her alter it.

'I know when I'm beaten,' she said, infusing a note of

light raillery into her voice. 'But I thought the days of caveman tactics were long past.'

Sonia laughed, poured another cup of coffee and handed it to her brother. 'Here, drink this, or you'll frighten Luce off.'

Which certainly didn't sound as though Sonia was keeping any marriage a deep dark secret.

It was an odd situation, made more tense by Conn's air of watchful patience, but they had lunch, and then, when the dishes had been done and Luce's baggage transferred into the car, she thanked her host and hostess for their hospitality, receiving, to her considerable surprise, a swift hard hug from Sonia.

'Wishing you luck,' Conn said sardonically as they pulled away.

'I like your sister.'

'Don't sound so surprised. She's not in the least like her brother.'

A small silence elapsed before Luce said quietly, 'You've changed.'

'I made a decision last night.'

'I saw you,' she told him, keeping her eyes firmly fixed on the road ahead. 'I couldn't sleep either.'

His sideways glance was as swift and sharp as a rapier. 'Why?'

'Oh, overtired, I suppose. It was a strange evening.'

He smiled grimly. 'An understatement.'

'Why are we going to the beach?' she asked.

'Because I think it's about time we put our cards on the table.'

A pulse began to beat hectically in her throat. 'What—what do you mean?'

'Just that I went into Whangarei this morning and got Faith to find the magazine that you were reading just before you tried to splatter your brains out on the stairs two years ago. We're going to go through it and see what's in it.'

Pulse beats were drumming in her ears now, making

it impossible for her to hear. 'But I've read it,' she said at last. 'Conn, that's no use. I tried that before—while I was in the hospital.'

'We'll try it again.'

He was inflexible, so determined that she said no more, but watched her hands clench and unclench in her lap all the way to the beach, while fear rose like a black cloud to hide her from the rest of the world.

Once in the beach house Conn poured her a glass of lime juice, sat down beside her on the sofa and dropped the magazine into her lap. Luce flinched, suppressing a startled cry. It was thick and glossy, superbly decorated by photographs and advertisements for jewellery and country houses and perfume. Luce stared down at the cover, thinking with distaste that the model had that air of dated smartness common to magazines of the type. An immense distaste for the thing filled her.

'Let's go through it, page by page.'

Conn's voice was inflexible. Casting him a look of complete dislike, she opened it at the first page.

An hour later she said raggedly, 'That's it, then.'

'No, there are a few more pages.'

'Only advertisements.'

His gaze was a warning, hard, merciless. 'Keep going, Luce. There's still the gossip pages.'

'Gossip?' There were, too, not the advertisements she had assumed there to be but several pages of tightly written paragraphs interspersed with photographs. Her fingers trembled against the shiny pages. She could feel the darkness pressing at the closed doors of her mind, the sinister, terryifying strength of it lurking there, waiting for her to remember.

Her voice was a thread of sound. 'I can't—I *won't*! Conn, please don't make me. Please. . . .'

There was no softness in the green gaze, no gentleness to ease the hard lines of his face. He looked like a devil, arrogantly confident, forcing his will to overcome hers. 'You must,' he said calmly. 'You know you must, Luce.

Come on, you have the courage and spirit and strength.'

Luce drew a deep sobbing breath. Hatred for him almost overwhelmed her; he had hunted and pursued her, driving her into this corner from which there was no escape.

'Read it,' he insisted, and with an exhalation of breath that came too close to a despairing cry she began to read.

Trivia, all of it, uneasily familiar, the first page, then the second. Darkness pressed through the doors now, advancing with a rush on evil cat feet. Luce turned her head, met Conn's icily implacable gaze and felt beads of sweat form at her temples. More than anything she longed for comfort, but he made no move to touch her, said nothing.

It was a small paragraph. 'Conn Ramsay, well-known playwright, escaped death by inches a week ago when a drunken driver demolished his car. Not so lucky was his companion, well known society hostess Nita Laurenson, who died before help could reach them. . . .'

There was more, but the darkness pounced, crushing her beneath an agony of disillusionment which forced her voice from her throat in a choked cry of despair.

Then he touched her; she was caught and encompassed by his arms as he rocked her gently back and forth, resting his cheek on the bright hair while she moaned in pain too intense for tears.

After a long time she pulled away. Instantly his arms dropped. She looked down at the magazine, crumpled on the slate floor.

'So that's where you got the scar,' she said dully. 'How, Conn?'

'Trying to get her out.' The gaily flowered cushion of the sofa moved; she could feel the cane creak as he relaxed into the back. His voice was cool, without expression. 'She was caught in the car. Conscious. By the time the rescue services arrived she was beyond help.'

'But you tried.'

'Oh, yes, I tried.'

As he had tried to help her, because some part of him, perhaps the last part free of cynicism, felt some sort of obligation.

'Damn you,' she whispered. 'Why couldn't you leave me alone? I was happy—I was happy here, until you came.'

'No, you weren't. Don't try to fool yourself, Luce, you barely existed. God, when I saw you on the beach I couldn't believe it was the same girl. You'd retreated into an icy shell. You, who'd been wilful, ardent, infuriating—but so vividly, vibrantly alive! I could have wept for what you'd become.'

'So you determined to bring me back?'

The hard note of censure in her voice angered him, but beyond frowning he made no attempt to respond to it. 'Yes.'

'I want to go back to the flat.'

'Right.'

And that was that, except that when they got there Teresa was home, summoned from a friend's home by an imperious telephone call, and soon after Conn had left Mattie Jameson came by and gave her a sedative. It worked, but long before dawn Luce woke and while the sky to the east paled and the dawn chorus sang its praise for another fine day, she lay in a stiff agonised knot under the bedclothes and remembered, shaking, clenching her teeth together to prevent the sobs from bursting forth and waking the others.

So vivid the memories were, as though her subconscious had kept them freshly dusted, ready for instant use. Her father, charming, weak, superbly good-looking, who had kept her at a boarding school because she reminded him that she had survived the plane crash in which his wife had died. Luce had only been three when it happened, but that memory too was mint clear, overlaid only slightly by the remembrance of the long flight

to Australia two years ago and the subsequent shorter
hop across the Tasman.

On those flights she had been too shattered by the
pain of disillusionment to give way to the phobia caused
by that fatal crash. She knew now why Conn had taken
her up in the little blue and white Cessna, knew too that
she would never again feel the sick panic which the mere
thought of flying had once engendered in her. One way
to rid oneself of a phobia, apparently, was to hit the
depths of despair and then force oneself into the phobic
situation.

How old had she been when her father had married
Nita? Ten or eleven, she estimated, a thin plain little
creature, all eyes and bones. Nita had been quite a
kindly stepmother, buying her elaborate presents for
birthdays and Christmas, occasionally appearing at
sports days and prize-givings, an enviable, dazzling
creature.

For Nita was beautiful, dark and sultry and fine-
boned with an elegance which owed only a little to the
fact that she was incredibly wealthy, able to buy superb
clothes and pamper herself. To the youthful Luce she
had seemed like a fairy princess, gay and glittering, a
little larger than life.

Inevitably Luce left school; even then, things had gone
along quite well. Nita made great play with the words,
'My beautiful stepdaughter,' insisted on an allowance
and was charming to her when they saw each other,
which was rarely. Luce spent her time discovering
London and was well content. Deeply grateful as she
was it took her father's unexpected death of a heart-
attack and her meeting with Conn Ramsay to destroy
the fragile relationship between the two women.

It all came back to Conn, careless, arrogant Conn
with his harsh cynicism and immense attraction. Slow
tears squeezed through Luce's lashes as she remembered
the very first time she had seen him. Nita was at a health
clinic so that Luce was alone in the big London house

when he called. He had looked at her with such speculative appreciation that she had blushed, laughing yet
shy.

'Good God!' When he smiled the charm leapt into
life, subjugating her. 'But are you enchanting! I'd
thought you a gawky schoolgirl.'

'Beside Nita I am.'

He frowned. 'Hardly, my girl,' he said drily. 'Tell me,
what do you do with yourself all day?'

'Oh—nothing.' With unerring aim he had struck a
sore point. She wanted to get a job, but her stepmother
had laughed at her, pointing out with kindly scorn that
she was trained for nothing.

Because Luce was still a little in awe of Nita she had
acquiesced, disliking the useless feeling but unable to
find a way to achieve her desire.

'Nothing?' The green gaze mocked her. 'Just a little
social butterfly?'

'Not just any social butterfly,' she retorted sweetly,
made pert by anger. 'A very special one.'

He laughed. 'Then come out to lunch with me. I need
entertaining.'

Hardly a flattering invitation, but even then she must
have been in the grip of the fierce attraction he had for
her. Whatever it was, she had responded to the amused
challenge in his expression with a forwardness Nita certainly would never have recognised.

That lunch had been the beginning of it all.

She had fallen headlong in love with him, making no
attempt to hide her feelings, and although he had been
aloof at first, sardonically amused by her transparency,
that had changed over the weeks. Even then she had
known that he didn't love her, but she had made him
tremble with desire and in her innocence she had
thought that love would follow.

God, how childish she had been, thinking that she
loved enough for two! He had tried to warn her, but she
had not believed him. Lost in the first experience of

intense physical desire, she was too naïve to realise that her hero-worship had transformed him into the Prince Charming of her adolescent dreams. Looking back now she could see how she had backed him into a corner, forcing him to choose between marrying her or allowing the inevitable to happen and destroying her innocence. Even then he had been brutally honest with her, but she had refused to admit that her dreams of lifelong happiness were built on the flimsiest of all foundations, desire.

At last, one evening when she had told him again how much she loved him, he had laughed, and kissed her with an ever deepening passion which aroused sensations of such overpowering desire that she had made no protest when he began to remove her clothes.

She had no excuse, she knew what was happening and she didn't care, offering him her body with the same innocent abandon that characterised all her dealings with him. But although he drove her mad with his expert caresses he still did not take her, not even when she asked him to, pressing herself against him in an agony of need.

'Oh no,' he said thickly, his mouth hot against the sensitive skin of her breast. 'No, you beautiful little wanton, I'm not going to get myself into a situation like that. I don't mind initiating you into the delights of heavy petting, but that's as far as it goes.'

He had meant to hurt, and he had, the brutal words flicking her like the lash of a whip. Furiously, her whole being one vast ache of longing, she slapped his face, watching with satisfaction as the dark skin flamed red where her palm had hurt it.

'Go to hell!' she seethed, sick with frustration.

'My way,' he taunted, and touched her with sensuous gentleness until she arched against him, lost.

'You're going to lead some poor devil one hell of a life.' His voice was derisory and he smiled with cruel malice. 'The morals of an alley cat and beauty to match.

You wouldn't care if I took you now, would you?'

'I want you to,' she muttered, pressing hot little kisses against the skin she had marked with her anger. 'Please, Conn. I love you so much. . . .'

He laughed at that, holding her away so that he could see her. Her hair had been longer then, uncut for years, and the fine tendrils veiled the white perfection of her shoulders in a tantalising cloud. His glance hardened, became fixed and glittering as it lingered on the high, young breasts, the narrow waist and the symbolic circle of her hips.

'You don't love me,' he said, but his voice was strangely distant as though he was repeating a lesson well learned. 'You want me to make love to you. There is a difference.'

Just to hear him say the words stimulated her into a feverish hunger. 'I love you,' she muttered obstinately, and put his hand on to her heart so that he could feel it throbbing. 'Can't you feel it? It beats for you.'

'For me now,' he told her, cynicism tightening his mouth. 'Next week it could be someone else. Luce, you're an enchanting and very sexy little girl, but you're going to end up as hardboiled as Nita if you keep on like this.'

'You—you started it.'

He nodded, the exciting glitter dying as he looked into her mutinous frustrated face. 'Yes, darling, I did, and believe me, I'm regretting it. I wanted to see how far you would go.'

'I suppose I'm shocking you.' Pain almost overcame her desire, but when he moved to release her she whimpered and clutched his shoulders, pressing herself against him in an agony of need only part of which was physical.

His sigh ruffled the wisps of hair about her temples. 'My dear, I'm unshockable. You're very sweet and I suppose if I didn't suffer from the remnants of a conscience I'd take what you're so generously offering and when I tired of you go my way without a care. But I do care, enough to draw back now.' His hand came up and began to stroke her hair back from her flushed face, moving slowly in the age-old gesture of comfort.

'But why?' she choked. 'Why won't you love me? I know I've no experience, but I'll learn. And I do love you, I do.'

'Hell, Luce!' Patience gone, he pushed her away from him, forcing her to lie still so that he could look at her, the contempt and anger in his gaze stripping her of what little pride she had left. 'Look at you,' he said harshly. 'Eighteen, aren't you, pretty as a picture, offering your virginal self without a qualm to a man whose only interest in you is sexual. What are you going to be like in ten years' time? Tough as old boots, slightly scarred from one or two abortions, possibly too fond of the bottle or smoking pot, still with that hungry look in your eyes. Is that what you want?'

'Of course it's not. . . .' Her voice trailed away into silence. How could she say that her dreams of the future involved him, centred on him, relied on him? So lost in love was she that she could not imagine a future without him. His words hurt, but even more painful was the cold accusation in his expression, the disdain with which his finger touched her body as he emphasised his words.

'Then what?' he pressed.

Colour flooded her skin. Not for anything would she reveal her innermost hopes to his scorn.

'Nita should be doing her best to marry you off,' he said after a moment. 'She could do it if she put herself out a bit.'

A shiver touched her skin. 'I don't want to get married,' she said pleadingly. 'I only want you, Conn.'

'But I don't want you.' He observed her involuntary flinch with hard eyes, his expression so remote that it chilled her into silence. 'O.K.,' he admitted when the silence had lengthened into tension, 'I do want you. You could quite easily drive me mad. You'd drain me of everything if I let you, and when I decided to end things—as I would, my boredom threshhold is low—you'd weep and plead and get pregnant or have a nervous breakdown or sleep with anyone in sight and blame me. That kind of publicity I can do without. I don't have affairs with teenage virgins.'

'Who do you have affairs with?' she asked bitterly, hating him and wanting him, loving him and loathing him for his cruelty.

'With mature, experienced women who don't make the mistake of thinking they love me. He pulled her up and held her against him so that when he spoke she could feel his lips against her forehead. 'With women who know how to conduct an affair, Luce. Believe me, I'm flattered that you should have picked me to be your first love, but it wouldn't work.'

'Don't tell me I'll thank you one day.' The words were bitter accusations. She felt the skin tighten across his shoulders as the muscles beneath grew taut, but his self-control was superb as ever.

'No, I won't tell you that,' he said and she could tell from the sound of his voice that he was smiling. 'You'll probably always hate me, but believe me, Luce, that's better than thinking you love me.'

When she sat up he leaned back into the cushions and watched her, still smiling, as she straightened her clothes and put on those which he had dropped on to the floor. And the smile had stayed there until she said icily, 'Nita is having a party at home. I'm going to go back there, pick out a man I like the look of, and then I'm going to take him up to my bedroom and make love with him, pretending that he's you.'

Conn laughed at that. 'Brave words, but you haven't the right sort of morals for that kind of carry-on.'

'Why don't you come with me and see for yourself?'

He still didn't believe her, but of course he took her home, and once there, he came inside. Even then, even though Nita greeted him with fulsome pleasure, she had

had no inkling. Perhaps she had been so buoyed up with her resolution to finally bring him to heel that she would have noticed nothing, anyway.

Once there she had ignored him although it nearly tore her heart out to do so. The man she chose was an actor, a handsome, rather conceited young man who was slightly awed by the wealth and sophistication of Nita's circle. He had been easy to flirt with, and when she had suggested that he come up and see the portraits in the big gallery he had agreed eagerly.

By then she was appalled at what she had planned; horrified too that this obsession with Conn could make her behave in so uncharacteristic a manner, but she set her jaw, determined to carry out her plan.

She had shown him the portraits, and had submitted to his kisses and groping hands with as much fortitude as she could summon up, but the sound of voices was extremely welcome; by the time Conn and several others arrived she and the actor were busy admiring the paintings collected by her father.

She had been acutely aware of Conn's eyes on her, cool and contemptuous, but had ignored him. Damn him! He thought nothing of her, why should he care what she did?

On the way down she and the actor trailed behind, keeping their voices soft. She wanted Conn to think that they were having an intimate conversation, although it was really of the utmost banality.

Her resolve had faltered; she knew that she could no more go through with it than subject herself to the horrors of flying again. A few minutes later she chose her time and slipped quietly up the stairs to her room.

Once there she got out of her clothes and pulled on a transparent nightgown and barely less transparent wrap. Brushing her hair, she gazed into the mirror and ached with the knowledge that she loved Conn and he would never love her. When the door opened behind her and he walked in she gaped, but recovered herself swiftly, ignoring the stifling press of heartbeats in her throat.

'What the hell are you doing?'

He smiled and her blood ran cold. 'Don't you know? Young Fanning has just been put into a taxi, drunk, so rather than see you frustrated I decided to take his place.'

'I beg your pardon?'

'That was what you arranged, wasn't it, as you were coming down the stairs?' He approached and stood behind her, his hands on her shoulders, looking at her in the mirror. His lashes were lowered so that all she could see of his eyes was a green glitter as they roamed her reflection. 'As you're so determined to rid yourself of your virginity I might as well take it. It will be a new experience for me. After all, you did say you were going to pretend that you were making love to me—this way, my sweet, you'll be able to concentrate entirely on what I want you to do.'

Very slowly he pulled her to her feet, turned her and kissed her, his arms hard across her back. Slowly, drugged by his nearness, Luce lifted her hands to either side of his face and opened her mouth beneath his, feeling the hardening of his body against her as desire overcame his contempt. At least, this response was hers.

'Ah God,' he whispered shakenly, lifting his head, 'what am I going to do with you, Luce?'

'Make love to me, please, Conn.'

He groaned, his fingers gentling as they roved across her back, pulling her closer to him so that she could feel just how much he wanted her.

'Not like this, not here.'

'I won't—I'll try not to be a nuisance, not to get in the way of your work,' she whispered frantically, instinct warning her that for once she had him at a disadvantage. 'I love you so much, but I won't expect anything more from you than you want to give me.'

He held her close saying savagely, 'You don't love me, you little fool, you want me. This is infatuation, calf love, lust, oh, call it what you will. It's madness. You don't even know me.' He held her away, the green eyes very cold and piercing. 'Promise me you'll never again do what you planned to do tonight.'

Her instinct was to promise him whatever he asked, but she knew she must not. 'No,' she retorted sullenly. 'You—you make me ache with wanting. If I can't have you, I'll find someone else.'

'Like a cat on heat.' His mouth tightened into anger, fingers moving on the fragile bones of her shoulders with cruel force.

'If I am then it's your fault!'

His laugh was reckless, almost defiant. 'Yes, I suppose it is. I knew you were trouble the first time I saw you; if I'd had any sense I'd have left London the next day. O.K., little cat, we'll get married. But we'll do it my way.'

And Luce had been so thrilled that she hadn't demurred when he insisted on secrecy, especially from Nita. If she thought about it at all she supposed he wanted to avoid publicity; after all, they were both news and there would be a horde of reporters spoiling things if their engagement became public knowledge.

The register office wedding was a little bleak, but Luce wore a white dress and carried flowers, and her radiant happiness cast its own glamour over the scene. And although Conn hadn't done much more than kiss her since the night he had told her they'd marry she knew that when they were together he would make love to her, and once he was hers she was confident that she could make him so happy that he would never want to leave her.

Luce moaned into her pillow, appalled by the naïvety of her eighteen-year-old self. How incredibly young she had been, how reckless!

But how happy, happier than ever before or since in her life, those few days between his capitulation and their wedding. The only flaw in her happiness had been that he refused to allow her to tell Nita, who had been kind to her in her fashion and who would possibly be hurt at being overlooked.

So before leaving for the register office she had left a note for Nita, elaborately casual, telling her. She hadn't told Conn what she had done; she knew that he would be angry, but it seemed so ungracious to leave Nita without a word.

The wedding was late in the day and afterwards Conn took her out to dinner. She had been excited, thrilled, bubbling with laughter and love and joy. A joy which was a vivid singing strength in her bones and her blood and her heart because she was Conn's wife and nothing could hurt her ever again.

And then, only five minutes after they had returned to his flat, Nita arrived.

Even now Luce could not recall the scene which followed without a return of the nausea which has assailed her then. Breathing deeply in an attempt to overcome it, she relaxed into limpness, her eyes fixed on the luminous dial of her watch. Soon it would be daylight and she would get up and go to work.

Lying there, she hated Conn with a fierce corrosive passion, wishing that he had died instead of Nita, that he had never lived, never wanted her enough to embark on that mockery of a marriage. It had been because of the responsibility he felt for her, but it would have been less cruel had he got out of her life. She would have wept, but at least he would not have scarred her so badly that her subconscious forced her into hiding. Ironically it was his uncharacteristic softer side which had done the permanent damage.

He had known what she had done even before Nita stepped inside. Luce shuddered at the memory of that savagely scornful look he had directed at her.

It had warned her that something was very wrong, but she still had not known what lay behind her stepmother's icy pallor and his withdrawal. As she stood

staring from one to the other Nita stripped off her gloves
and put them carefully on a table. Then she smiled. It
was easy to see that the smile was summoned up and
held on her lips only by willpower.

'Unlike you to have wasted an opportunity, Conn,'
the older woman said calmly, 'but I can see that I'm in
time. She looks tousled but still hungry. Sit down, Luce.
You're going to need some support.'

'Conn?' Luce looked helplessly at him, saw him smile
as he leaned against the door frame, and at the cold-
blooded cruelty of that smile her blood ran icily through
her veins.

'Do as she says, Luce.' That was all he said, all that
he needed to say.

Limply she sat down, aware now of the tension that
sparked between her husband and her stepmother but
still unable to understand.

The silence that followed seemed to fill the room,
pressing against her eardrums as she watched Nita, conscious of the glittering glance from Conn's narrowed
eyes.

After a long moment Nita said abruptly, 'There's no
way I can think of to be tactful about this, Luce. Are
you aware that Conn and I are lovers? We have been,
for quite a few years.'

The blood retreated from her skin. Very slowly she
turned her head in blind appeal. Conn said nothing, but
his expression was closed and watchful as his gaze met
hers.

'Conn?' It was a plea, barely loud enough to be
heard.

'Listen to her, Luce,' he said relentlessly. 'Why should
it make any difference to us? You love me, so you've
told me a hundred times.'

The savage cynicism of his tone hit her like a blow.
For a moment she thought she was going to faint, but
somewhere deep inside her was an unconquerable core
of strength. It was this which kept her head high.

'For God's sake, Conn!' Nita spoke angrily, her dark glance almost pitying as it rested on Luce's face. 'You're a cruel bastard. I gather you told her nothing about us.'

'It didn't seem important,' he said indifferently.

Nita winced but said, 'Perhaps not to you, but it obviously is to Luce. And to me, I might add. You could at least have told me that you wanted nothing more to do with me before you married her.'

'So I might.' The green eyes rested on the older woman's exquisite face, moved insolently down the pure line of her throat and breast.

And Nita flushed while naked hunger lit the depths of her eyes. Her fingers clenched on themselves. Luce felt a revulsion so intense that it almost made her ill. Although Conn had made no attempt to deny it she had hoped against hope that Nita lied, but that involuntary movement of her hands revealed it all. The older woman was sick for him, her desire a voracious hunger that drove her to this confrontation even though she must know that she was damaging herself and whatever she and Conn had shared.

'Are you all right?' Nita stared at her. 'You look as though you're going to faint.'

Conn came away from the door with a lunge, bent over the back of the chair and twisted his fingers in the hair at the nape of her neck, smiling that fierce smile. 'You're not going to faint, are you, Luce?' he asked with cold, controlled menace.

Pain brought tears to her eyes as it dragged her back from the abyss of unconsciousness. 'No,' she said numbly, 'don't, Conn. Please,' as he showed no signs of releasing her.

Even Nita looked fearful. 'Leave her alone,' she said half contemptuously. 'For heaven's sake, Conn, she's only a child! Why on earth did you marry her?'

'A quixotic impulse of chivalry,' he answered coolly, freeing his fingers from her hair. He sat down beside Luce on the sofa and took her hand in his, his narrowed

glance hawklike and predatory as it rested on the pale
pure profile. 'And perhaps I fancied the idea of my own
little virgin.'

By now Luce was barely functioning. Locked in the
talons of a pain so intense that it robbed her of initiative
and willpower, she concentrated on staying conscious.

Through a mist she heard Nita say with angry despair,
'You're a cruel swine, Conn. I hope you weren't planning on any money, because she's got none. Her father
was penniless when I married him and he died penniless.
She'll be a drain on your resources.'

'My resources are adequate.' Again that imprisoning
glance. 'And we intend to live very economically for
some time, don't we, darling? We won't be going out
much.'

The savage taunt made every muscle in her body con-
tract. Lifting a tormented gaze to meet the hard derision
of his, she said huskily, 'Conn, *don't*.'

'Don't what?' He lifted the hand he held captive,
rested the pulse spot in the wrist against his lips.

Nita drew a sharp breath, colour appearing in her
cheeks as two harsh spots. 'Don't mind me!' she exclaimed.

'I thought you'd never go.' His voice was cruelly
casual. 'Let yourself out,' he commanded after a
moment.

White beneath her superb make-up, Nita closed her
eyes, then swung towards the door. 'I hope you enjoy
each other,' she spat out between her teeth. 'And when
you get tired of her, Conn, come back to me. It will give
me great pleasure to throw you out.'

He laughed as he rose and walked across the room to
stop in front of her, tall and perfectly balanced, his aura
of magnetism a combination of looks and personality
and superb self-confidence. Nita flushed, staring at him,
held by the green arrogance of his gaze. Her lip quivered;
Luce saw her stepmother's self-confidence evaporate
under that coldly ironic gaze. Nervously the older

woman licked her lips and then, whimpering, pressed herself against him, the soft mouth ardent and seeking as it touched his.

Luce wanted to close her eyes, but she could not move. Aware that she had seen him humiliate Nita, use her need to bring about an abject surrender, she winced.

'Damn you,' her stepmother stammered frenziedly. 'Damn you, Conn!'

She almost ran out of the room; the door slammed to behind her like a prison gate.

'I'll make sure that we're not disturbed again.' Conn said, as if her visit had been in the nature of a minor nuisance.

When he came back into the room Luce hadn't moved. She sat very primly, knees and ankles together, her hands clasped loosely in her lap, her head bent slightly forward to expose the vulnerable nape of her neck.

'Why did you leave her a note?'

'I thought I owed her that, at least,' she answered slowly. 'I've been very stupid, haven't I?'

'Incredibly.' He tipped her chin, forcing the white mask of her face back to meet his gaze. 'I suppose you want me to explain things to you?'

It hurt to meet the cool derision of his eyes, to realise that he had no intention of making things right. Perhaps because he couldn't; Nita had told the truth and there was nothing he could say that would ever return things to the way they had been. Or the way she had assumed them to be, she corrected herself, bitterness darkening her eyes as he ran his thumb across the soft line of her lower lip.

In spite of her disillusionment he still had the power to stir her blood. The pulse in her throat accelerated as her lashes fluttered down to hide the shameful desire that leaped into life within her.

'Do you hate me?' he asked, a note of lazy sensuality in the deep voice.

A flash of defiance lit her eyes. 'Yes!'

'Just as Nita does.'

Colour fled from her cheeks. Her eyes flew open as she struck at the hand which held her prisoner. As if the violent movement released some corresponding violence within him he grinned and pushed her down into the cushions, holding her wrists pinioned with one hand while the other pulled her clothes free, wrenching the fragile material until it gave and she was lying in the remnants of her pretty little wedding dress.

'What's happened to the love you swore so ardently?' Conn jeered, his eyes moving from the rapid movement of her breasts to the flimsy pants which were the only remaining barrier to his lust. 'Hardly the earthshaking emotion you considered it if it's extinguished by the discovery of a mistress. Surely true love—the kind you professed to feel—should be able to take that sort of thing in its stride. Think of Patient Griselda!'

Luce twisted, anger forcing despair into abeyance, only ceasing when she realised that her writhing body excited him. If only he would explain—tell her that he didn't love Nita, that he had not made love to her recently.

'Conn,' she said suddenly, urgently, 'I'm not—why didn't you tell me? Why?'

'There were reasons.'

He spoke absently, as if the words were mere mouthing of sounds divorced from reason or intent, but the green darkness of his gaze was merciless, an open avowal of his intention to take her.

Luce knew that she could not allow him to humiliate her so, as if she meant nothing more to him than poor Nita, merely a willing body to plunder. Certain no longer that she loved him, or whether she was, like her stepmother, in thrall to a sexuality she could not resist, she knew nothing except that to submit to his passion would be a humiliation greater than any other.

'What reasons?' she asked, hoping to divert him.

He smiled, and a flame leaped to life in the depths of his eyes, searing, all-encompassing and contemptuous. 'My darling,' he said insolently, bending his head so that the words warmed the skin across her throat, 'my dearest wife, you swore to love me, lured me into this marriage with your violent love. Now prove it to me.' His mouth moved, burning into the pale silk of her skin, the tip of his tongue setting her nerves on fire. 'Or, by God, I'll make you wish you'd never been born,' he finished in soft chilling tones before his lips closed over the softness of her breast.

A surge of desire so intense that it shook her entire body made her gasp. The grip on her wrists loosened, then he released them and slid his arm behind her back as he lowered himself on to her, imprisoning her beneath him.

'Love me,' he said thickly into her mouth before plundering it in a kiss which set a thousand fires flickering through her veins.

It was agony to refuse him, heart and body against her brain, and for long moments the voice of reason faded as his mouth and hands explored her body, seducing, incredibly erotic, revealing to her how sensual a response he could evoke from her. Heat flushed her skin; she felt the hard weight of his body on hers with a joy she could not repress, but she refused to abandon herself to it, aware through the mists of desire that Conn was using his expertise to reduce her to a mindless submission when she would be no more than the slave of her physical reactions.

Slowly, with an effort of will so immense that she grew weak with it, Luce forced herself to lie motionless in his arms, to close her ears to the husky voice as he whispered endearments against her skin. Her only hope was to be passive; she could feel the leashed strength in him and knew that if she resisted him he would subdue her to his will.

Nita's face, tortured, shamed as it had been when she

had kissed him, was imprinted on her closed lids. With a stifled sob she turned her head into the cushion, clenching her fists to stop them from responding to his practised seduction. He appeared not to notice her withdrawal; possibly he was so intent on his own gratification that he gave no thought to her reactions or needs.

Then he proved her wrong. Gently, as though her skin was fragile, he began to touch her, exploring her body and all its secret places. His eyes closed, his expression was absorbed, almost tender, and she shivered, knowing that against his tenderness she had no armour.

Instantly his lashes lifted. He subjected her to a long scrutiny; gradually his eyes hardened as he took in her averted face, the taut tension of her muscles beneath the smooth skin. It took all her willpower to prevent herself from welcoming him in that most intimate of embraces. Her body was wrought to a fever pitch by his nearness and she knew now that if he did not take her she would be left in a state of extreme frustration that would be agony. But still Nita's face mocked her, its blind desire a hideous parody of her own reactions.

'So,' Conn said quietly, his hand closing with hurtful emphasis over her breast. 'Is that love you prated so endlessly about not quite as limitless as you'd thought? Having second thoughts, my dearest?'

'You're hurting,' she whispered.

He smiled, and lifted his hand to clasp her throat, the lean fingers tightening momentarily. 'Answer my question, Luce.'

'Why didn't you tell me?'

Again that narrow, savage smile. 'Perhaps I wanted to test that love you were so talkative about. If you love me only half as much as you said you did you wouldn't care how many mistresses I've had.'

Staring up into the inscrutable mask, she suddenly knew why he hadn't bothered to reveal Nita's place in his life. He had been so confident of her love that he thought it unnecessary. Anger sparked within her, grew to a flame, that coloured her cheeks and darkened her eyes into stormy pools.

'Perhaps it wasn't love,' she stated in a tight, hard voice. 'Perhaps it was just infatuation after all.'

He lifted his brows. 'Almost certainly. Although infatuation shouldn't prevent you from enjoying your wedding night, my sweet.'

The amused cynicism in his voice brought her temper very close to combustion. Ignoring the danger she was in, she blurted, 'I wish I'd never met you!'

'You can't wish that more than I do,' he responded smoothly. 'Now, are you going to be sensible, or shall I go and find myself another partner for the night?'

'*Sensible*! No, I damned well won't be sensible! I think you've got a hell of a nerve, expecting everything to be just the same as it was before. Of all the insensitive——!'

The swift violent pressure of his body stunned her into silence. For a moment such ferocious anger blazed from his face that she really thought he was going to kill her. Then it vanished, to be replaced by the same bored lack of interest with which he had looked at her stepmother. No doubt he looked at every importunate woman in his life just like that, she thought, swallowing with difficulty as he released her aching throat and sat up.

'Save your childish rantings to go with your childish protestations of undying love,' he said coldly as he moved towards the door.

Left cold and aching for him, she asked huskily, 'Where—where are you going?'

'To Nita. Where else?'

Her hand flew to her throat. 'She—she won't take you in,' she whispered.

Very slowly he turned, looked her over from head to toe, his eyes flat and hard as pebbles. 'Don't you think so?' he asked politely. 'You really are very juvenile, darling. The body of an extremely enticing woman, but the mind of a schoolgirl. Of course she'll have me back. Let me know when you grow up, Luce. We might be able to have fun together.'

He had gone then, and after twelve hours of waiting Luce had taken her bags and a taxi to Heathrow.

To an oblivion which she had always recognised as merciful. Damn him, she thought, lashing herself into futile anger. How dared he! Playing God, reintroducing her to a pain which gripped her so that it hurt to breathe, when as soon as he set eyes on her again he must have realised that she was happier in her ignorance.

Perhaps he had wanted to make her unhappy; even as she flinched at the idea she knew that it was not true. Not even Conn would deliberately seek that sort of revenge, though he had proved himself cruel enough. There had been truth in his tones when he had told her that she had looked only half alive without her memory. Reluctantly she admitted that he was correct; in ten years' time she might even be thankful for his determination to drag her from the refuge her subconscious had provided for her.

CHAPTER EIGHT

'You look different,' Teresa said seriously, that evening, pushing another cup of coffee across the table to her. 'I thought you'd be happier—but you've gone all wan.'

Luce smiled, aware that it was a pale effort but unable to summon up anything brighter. 'Life was pretty desolate for me two years ago. I seem to have two sets of memories, and the ones I lost are just as vivid as the more recent. So are the emotions.'

It was obvious that both her friends were extremely curious about her past, equally obvious that neither was going to ask a single question. Probably Mattie Jameson had instructed them. The coffee was delicious, hot and strong and aromatic. Luce blew away a drift of steam and sipped, then said softly:

'Conn and I are married.'

Teresa was astounded, but Faith merely nodded.

'Not surprised?' Luce asked.

'No, not really. He's been incredibly possessive right from the start. I assumed that at the very least you'd been engaged.'

Teresa said urgently, 'But when you were examined you were *virgo intacta*, Luce. What happened?' She bit her lip, pulling it in. 'Hell, that's hardly tactful, is it? Ignore me.'

'No, it's all right.' Luce's shoulders moved slightly beneath the thin straps of her camisole top. 'Immediately after the wedding we had a—a misunderstanding. I ran away. To Australia.'

'Why Australia?' Faith asked quietly, her expression calmly interested.

'My parents were both Australian; I was born there. I knew that a passport wasn't needed between there and

New Zealand, so when I reached Melbourne I booked a seat under a false name, dumped all my documents into a safe deposit box there and came over here. I disguised myself a bit—covered my hair with a scarf and wore sunglasses.'

Faith nodded. 'That's why they couldn't trace you, of course. Well, what now? Do you go back to England with him?'

'I don't think so.' Avoiding Teresa's disappointed gaze, Luce lowered her head to drink her coffee. After a moment she said, 'We should never have married. I was infatuated with him—and you grow out of that.'

'And he?'

Answering Faith's question was easy. With a wry smile Luce responded, 'He never loved me. He didn't pretend to. He married me because I threatened to do something stupid if he didn't.'

'I've heard a lot of funny things in my time,' Teresa snorted, unable to contain herself, 'but that's about the most ludicrous! I simply cannot imagine an arrogant, insolent devil like Conn Ramsay being blackmailed into anything! He'd be more likely to damn your eye and dare you to do your worst.'

Luce smiled with bitter irony. 'Oh, he has his weaknesses—pretty women being one. And for some reason I must appeal to what's left of his protective instinct.'

'I wouldn't have thought he possessed one.' Teresa's comment was aggressive; her fingers tightened around the handle of her coffee mug as if she wished it to be Conn's throat.

'You'd be surprised,' Luce told her lightly. 'Anyway, it's past history now. I'm grateful that he took the trouble to—to help me get my memory back.'

'As he was, no doubt, the reason for it going in the first place it was the least he could do.' Teresa was not going to be appeased. She had cast Conn as the villain of the piece and was now fiercely, protectively, on Luce's side.

Luce was warmed by her partisanship, but Faith's sensible outlook was almost certainly the one to strive for. Conn had helped her; now he could go back to England and forget about her. Amidst the pain that this thought brought her she was surprised to find a nostalgia for home. Her eyes strayed to the window. Outside Sweet Williams flowered thickly between great blue flag irises and the tall cones of a scarlet waratah; over the trellis that hid the small garden shed tumbled a glossy leaved creeper with big pink flowers, their deeper pink hearts exhaling sweetness on to the air. It was beautiful and she loved it. Yet she felt an urge to go back to the land she would always consider to be her home.

She could not, of course. Not as long as there was any possibility of seeing Conn, or reading about him. The coffee was tasteless in her mouth now, as she wondered how long it took to get over loving the wrong man. Two years of a new life had not changed her feelings for him except in degree. Oddly enough although she had not remembered him, her emotions had deepened. Given the same situation she would not act in the same way. She had been naïve and self-centred, but with the incredible effrontery of youth had chosen her man and allowed nothing to get in the way of her choice. It had been what she saw as his betrayal which had provoked her behaviour on their wedding night, and mixed up with that had been a badly dented pride. Had he coaxed her, or made some explanation, she would have given in.

But Conn, arrogant as ever, saw no need for explanations. He had made it quite obvious that he had no feelings left for Nita. As far as he was concerned that was explanation enough. And he, too, had been betrayed. Luce had been persistent in her demands on him, and he had married her because he thought that her love made her in some sense his responsibility. But at the first test of that love she had failed him, her moral and emotional blackmail exposed in all its shoddiness.

That was what hurt her now. Perhaps maturity, perhaps just the extra two years of living had made her adult enough to understand just how badly she had failed him. And it was not made any the easier to bear because he had been the first to betray, for when Nita had dropped her bombshell it had never occurred to Luce that there might be any explanation. She had condemned him instantly and he had known it.

It was later, when she was searching for a way to solace her hurt pride so that she could enjoy his lovemaking, that she had asked for an explanation. And his pride refused her as cruelly as she had refused him. If she had done nothing else, she thought now, she had certainly reinforced his cynical attitude towards humanity.

'Are you all right?'

She looked up at Teresa, banishing her sombre thoughts with a smile. 'Yes, I'm fine.'

'Well, what do you plan to do?'

Her shoulders lifted in a slight shrug. 'Nothing. I've made a new life for myself. If he wants an annulment or a divorce, whichever comes easiest, I don't care, he can go ahead and get it.'

'There's not a chance. . . .' Incurably romantic, Teresa felt her voice fade at the small cynical movement of Luce's lips.

'Not a hope.'

And such was the conviction in her voice that the other two women exchanged glances, and for the rest of the week Conn's name was not mentioned.

It was a long slow week, unseasonably cold for the first few days and then, as if the weather had relented, very hot and humid. On Monday Luce posted two letters thanking Sonia and the Stewarts for their hospitality, and then she tried to put Conn out of her mind.

During the day she almost managed it, only to spend long wakeful hours in the night tossing and turning while memories burned themselves into her brain.

By Saturday morning she was looking pale and exhausted, a fact which neither of her friends mentioned.

Over breakfast coffee Teresa asked without expression, 'What are you going to do today, Luce?'

'Tidy my room, and then I think I'll spend the afternoon at the Tennis Club. If I don't get some exercise I'll go mad.'

'Take up jogging,' Faith advised. 'Does Conn play tennis?'

Startled, Luce said, 'I don't know. Why?'

'Because he's just pulled up outside.' Faith poured more coffee, adding, 'He looks grim.'

'You don't have to go with him,' Teresa hissed like a conspirator in a bad spy film.

Bright coins of colour touched Luce's cheeks. For the first time in days she felt alive. 'He won't eat me.'

Grim he might have been feeling, but he hid it with his usual air of lazy cynicism, although his regard was watchful. Luce felt the old helplessness, summoned up her new maturity to overcome it. It could have been an awkward meeting, but Faith and Conn between them acted so normally that Teresa's hackles lowered and even Luce managed to give an unusually good imitation of her normal self.

He accepted coffee, complimented Faith on its excellence, and waited until everyone had relaxed before saying blandly, 'Luce, I've an invitation from Sonia to spend the day with her. Ryan and I are going fishing.'

Luce stared into her coffee, acutely conscious of everyone's eyes. The moment stretched until he laughed and said, 'Get your bag, idiot girl.'

And it was as simple as that. Although she was still tense in his company she knew only too well that she would rather be with him than not.

After they had gone a few miles Conn commented, 'You're looking washed out. Haven't you been sleeping?'

'Mattie gave me sedatives, but I don't like using

them.' She turned her head, looking directly at him. 'And no, I haven't been sleeping terribly well. How about you?'

He smiled. 'Not particularly. Still hating me?'

'Oh, yes.' It seemed safer to lie than to reveal the true state of her emotions.

Silence, then he remarked, 'I gather you've revealed all. Teresa looked at me as though I was one of the less attractive bacteria, and even Faith had a faint note of censure in her voice.'

'I told them that we were married and that things went wrong,' Luce returned huskily, hating the mockery in his voice. 'That's all.'

'You mean you managed to avoid awarding blame? I find that hard to believe.'

'Oh, don't be so bloody-minded! I didn't blame anyone, and I can't help it if they find me a fit subject for their maternal—or sisterly—instincts.'

'It's that pale, pure look, that air of being an ethereal, not quite mortal, almost faerie being that does it. When I first met you I thought you'd probably turn out to be a frigid little bitch; it was a surprise to discover all the instincts of a courtesan beneath that remote image.'

'Charming,' she retorted, bitterness tinging her voice. 'I'd have thought that someone as experienced as you would have recognised the signs.'

'By then it was too late.'

He spoke with such sombre intensity that she flinched, blinking rapidly to hide the stinging tears his cruelty caused. Perhaps that was why she missed the significance of the turning; it wasn't until five minutes later that suspicion hardened into certainty and she turned a white face towards him.

'You lied! This is the way to the beach. Sonia didn't invite me.'

'As it happens, she did, but I refused for you. We need to spend some time alone.'

She panicked then, hitting at him until he pulled off

the road and shook her into a sobbing submission, the white line around his mouth warning her that she had gone too far.

'Don't be so bloody stupid,' he ordered harshly. 'I'm not going to harm you, you silly little fool. Calm down. We need to talk, to come to some arrangement about the future, and the best place is on the beach, where we won't be interrupted.'

He waited until the choked sobbing quietened, then said more gently, 'Believe me, Luce, I don't want to cause you any more upset or pain, but you must see that we can't just leave things as they are now.'

Luce nodded, wiping her eyes. 'I'm sorry,' she said, putting a hand to her throat. 'Jolie said that, didn't she? *I'm sorry.* I think I knew then—that was why I fainted. The way she looked and spoke—it was the same way that Nita——'

Her hands were grasped, held firmly as he slid an arm around her shoulders and held her for a moment against him. 'I suppose you're terrified it will go again,' he said into her hair. 'Mattie said it's not likely.'

'You've spoken to her?' It was sweet to be held so comfortingly, but she pulled away, surprising an odd quirk to his lips as he looked down at her.

'Yes. She thinks that the shock of your father's death and your first violent passion combined with an equally violent disillusionment, on top of a hair-raising trip in a plane, possibly combined with a crack on the head, is a collection of circumstances unlikely to happen again.'

The extreme dryness of his voice won a reluctant smile from her, and after a moment she relaxed back into the seat.

Conn set the car in motion again and they were coming down through the patterned shade of the trees to where the little cove dreamed under the sky. Out to sea yachts in a race to the Bay of Islands lifted multicoloured sails to the wind, dipping and swaying like exotic butterflies against the wrinkled surface of the sea.

When Luce got out of the car she breathed deeply, welcoming the sensuous murmur of the waves, the warm caress of the breeze that lifted the pale tresses of hair across her temples.

'Do you want to swim?'

She shook her head. 'No, not yet.'

'Then come and sit down on the terrace.'

Her previous panic was forgotten. Conn seemed impersonal now, as though he had no further interest in her. A little piqued, she accepted a cold beer, lay back on a lounger and asked, 'How did you know I was here, Conn?'

'Sonia told me. She knew that I'd married and that it hadn't worked out, but nothing else, so she had no idea who you were, but you interested her and she mentioned you in one of her letters, as well as the fact that you'd lost your memory.' He smiled narrowly, watching her. 'I didn't believe it, of course. I thought you'd chosen that way to re-open communications. I was ready for a holiday, so I decided it would amuse me to come out here, appear to fall in with your plans and then leave you flat.' He shrugged, almost moodily.

'What made you change your mind?' she asked in stifled tones.

'When I realised that you really did have amnesia. That first day we met, to be precise. At the beach. You looked at me with those empty eyes, a little puzzled, very wary, like a kid threatened with a memory of a nightmare.' Restlessly he moved across to the edge of the terrace, staring out to sea for a long moment before turning back with self-mockery in his expression. 'I found I couldn't hate a child with no past.'

'Yet you weren't exactly kind to me.'

'No. I had to convince myself that you really were an amnesiac. I tried you out a little first.'

'The flight,' she said quietly.

He nodded. 'Yes. I knew of your phobia. That's why it took me so long to discover that you'd left England;

it simply never occurred to me that you'd fly. When I did—well, the trail was well cold. But your reaction to the flight convinced me. You were uneasy, but certainly not phobic, although the faint had me wondering, until I realised that you were more bewildered than I was about it. I knew then that you must have lost your memory completely. So I went back to see Dr Jameson and asked her if my probing would harm you.'

'Did you?'

Her astonishment was pronounced enough to make him frown.

'I realise that I've given you little reason to think highly of me,' he returned drily, 'but I didn't want to tip you over the edge into madness; you'd told me of the abyss you felt threatened you. Dr Jameson assured me that madness was the least of your worries. She agreed that I should try to help you regain your memory, and gave me an idea of what to do.'

'Make love to me.'

The darkness at the centre of his eyes deepened, drowning out the green. He smiled, not pleasantly. 'She said that a repetition of the events leading up to the trauma frequently freed the block. In this case making love to you didn't work, so I tried the magazine. She was convinced that the clue must be there.'

Before he finished speaking Luce had turned her head away so that he couldn't see the bleak desolation she knew must be mirrored in her eyes. 'And that worked,' she said, adding in as level tones as she could summon up, 'Why didn't you just go away and leave me, Conn? It would have been kinder.'

'You asked me that before. I'm not kind.' His voice was hard, but it softened slightly as he went on, 'Because you were only half a person. Experience, however painful, however hardly earned, is a gift, a precious gift. You're entitled to your experiences because what they are is what you are. We had some good times, Luce. Call your memory a repayment for those times.'

'It's more like a punishment for the bad,' she said, half under her breath.

His hand on her shoulder was merciless as he forced her round to face him. In a voice that revealed just how cruel he wanted to be he said, 'That's twice you've fallen for me, Luce. Don't argue. You know it's true,' as she opened her mouth to protest. 'You should have learned your lesson. The first time it happened you endowed me with virtues I don't possess, masked the response of your body with a whole series of false emotions and called this love. And because you thought that the fact that you were in love excused anything, you behaved like an amoral, wanton little animal. This time you've done a little better; you refused to let me take you because you knew something was wrong.' His smile twisted. 'Next time, you might well find whatever it is that you want. But it won't be with me. I'll organise a divorce as soon as I get back home.'

'A divorce?' Luce kept her glance on the button of his shirt straight in front of her eyes so that he shouldn't see just how shattered she was by his decision. 'Wouldn't an annulment be quicker?'

'Yes.' His hand moved gently to clasp her throat, tilting her chin so that she was forced to tip her face upwards to meet his gaze. From beneath her lowered lids she saw the hot possession of his expression, and a pulse leapt in her body. 'Yes, you know what I want,' he said softly. 'You've cost me a lot of time and trouble, Luce, and the one way you can repay me is by giving me what you promised so ardently two years ago. At that time I thought it was worth my freedom; let's see if I was right, shall we?'

He had hurt her before, almost killed her love for him, but she had never felt pain like this. It was like a knife in her heart, the cold calculated cruelty of it a savage violation of her very personality. Such agony had made her subconscious excise him from her life as though his memory was a growth that must kill her.

'No!' she bit out harshly, trying to pull away.

Immediately his fingers tightened until her head swam. 'Why not? You know you want me. And God knows I want you. I always have. An affair now could well set us both free.'

'If—if you take me——' Luce searched for the words to explain her meaning. Conn looked down at her, his eyes calculating and predatory.

'What?'

'I don't think I can ever be myself again.'

Miraculously the grip on her throat eased, but only to be replaced by his mouth burning against the skin. 'You've always dramatised yourself,' he murmured, his hands moving slowly down to rest on her hips. 'Perhaps that's why I appeal to you.'

'I mean it.' She held herself rigid, calling on every ounce of resistance to fight the insidious uprush of desire.

'Rubbish, darling. It's only because you're a virgin that you believe nonsense like that. Relax—I won't hurt you. God knows I've had enough experience to make it pleasurable.'

He pulled her on to the lounger beside him, wrenching at her sun-top and sliding it from her body with hands that trembled slightly when they met the gentle curves of her breasts. She was lost when his mouth followed, sick with a desire that weakened her. He knew how to arouse her, holding her up in his arms so that he could taste her breasts until she was faint with the hunger that only he could sate. When he undid the button on her shorts and pulling the wide mattress of the lounger on to the ground laid her on it she made no resistance, but her slumbrous eyes hid an expression in which pain and passion were equally mixed.

'God, but you're beautiful!' He stripped off and came down beside her, his eyes fever-bright, the hard exciting line of mouth and jaw brooking no further demur. Slowly, sensuously his hand fondled the secret parts of her body, moving caressingly across her stomach and the smooth firm skin of her thighs while his mouth sought hers, exploring within her parted lips in a kiss which presaged that other more intimate exploration which was inevitable now.

This was what he had done on the night of their marriage, using all of his expertise to bring her to a pitch of passion when she ached for the hard invasion of his body.

When his mouth lifted she whispered, 'Are you going to leave me now?'

He must have been remembering too, for he smiled against her mouth. 'No, I bloody near died of frustration, I'm not running that risk again. Hold me, Luce. Pretend you love me.'

Pretend! The breath caught in her throat, but she could no longer think sanely, and with a moan of submission she kissed the junction of neck and shoulder, using her hands to form the shape and size and feel of his body until at last their desire peaked and what had begun as sensual exploration ended in fleeting pain and ecstasy and exhaustion.

When Conn lifted himself away it felt as though the other half had been torn from her. Above them the seabirds still called, a mewing, lonely anthem for an act of love that left her hungrier than before. Sunlight wavered across them in golden coins through the leaves of a pohutukawa as the sun reached his zenith.

Luce looked at the man beside her, loving him with a love which had never died, and knew now that there could be nothing left for her in this life.

Unless . . . slowly her hand moved to lie across her stomach. Perhaps even now, the miracle of conception had occurred and she might yet have some solace in the black years ahead.

'We didn't think of that, did we?'

Her hand clenched into a fist. Acute as ever, Conn had known immediately what had lain behind the gesture. Now he was watching her, his expression too impassive to be natural.

'It's highly unlikely,' she said huskily.

'Nevertheless, we'd better decide whose responsibility it is.'

Hope flared in her breast. 'I don't know what you mean.'

'How long before you know whether or not you're pregnant?'

Frowning, she counted. 'About a month, I suppose, to be absolutely sure. Why?'

'Because no child of mine is growing up outside my orbit.'

Luce felt herself grow hot under his possessive gaze. Obviously he did not find being naked an embarrassment, but she did, and she made the discovery that a blush is highly visible.

'So,' he said, half jeering as he ran a finger from her throat to her navel, 'that gives me a month to sate myself with you. Think it will be long enough?'

She could have wept with the pain of her frustrated dreams, but kept tight control of the muscles of her face. The last thing she wanted was for him to read her heart as he seemed to be able to read her mind and as he definitely understood the reactions of her body.

'So if you can bear to get dressed,' he mocked, taking her assent for granted, 'we'll go back into Whangarei and you can pick up a few clothes and tell that boss of yours that you want your holidays now.'

Luce sat up, stunned and appalled. 'I can't! Not just like that. Graeme has been very good to me—I can't just walk out on him!'

'You did it to me,' Conn reminded her, smiling as the colour faded from her skin. 'But then you were only married to me, weren't you, not my employee. Once I'd have said that you had no principles at all, but I realise now that they're just different from other people's.'

'Like yours,' she said bitterly, turning away from him

to pick up her clothes. Resolution stiffened her back, steadied her voice as she went on calmly, 'I'm not going to move in with you, Conn. Quite frankly I don't think I can cope with more punishment.'

'Was that what it was?' The side of the lounger moved as he rolled towards her, preventing her movement by his favourite method of twining her hair through his fingers. 'Yet you didn't seem to hate it so much, my darling. In fact, if asked to describe your reactions I'd have to use words like unrestrained, or uninhibited—even wanton.'

The coldly ironic note in his voice brought a shudder to her skin, a physical reaction more easily coped with than the pit of black despair that had opened at her feet.

Without moving, for she could feel his desire to hurt beating against her, she acknowledged, 'You'd probably be right, too. I've never denied that I want you. But I wasn't referring to that.'

'What then?'

'Your constant taunts.' For a moment his fingers tightened painfully on the baby-soft tendrils at the base of her neck. She sat very still, her head held high by his grip, but the slump of her shoulders revealing the defeat he had inflicted on her. Slowly his fingers relaxed, began a sensuous stroking movement across her neck and shoulders. She shivered again, but this time with the desire which his gentleness invoked. His cruelty did not hurt as much as the fugitive tenderness he knew so well how to use.

'You're afraid of me, aren't you, Luce?'

She bit her lip. 'Not so much of you——' and stopped precipitately.

Moving with hypnotic gentleness, he turned her to face him. He was smiling, but without the undertone of savagery which frightened her; instead there was a kind of wry sympathy in his glance as he looked at her.

'As of yourself,' he said quite calmly. 'I know, believe

me. You frightened hell out of me two years ago. I didn't want the responsibility for your happiness dumped on to me, but there was no one else, was there. Nita couldn't have cared less, you didn't even have a close friend to help you pick up any pieces. I could see you treading a particularly wide and primrosy path to hell, seduced by the responses of that delectable body and your need for love.'

'So you married me,' she said on an indrawn breath.

'So I married you.' He moved, pulling her across to lie against him. A little breeze managed to find its way through the trees to caress them; it was hot, with the hard, fierce heat of midday, but against the dampness of her skin it felt cool. The noise of the gulls had died away. An early cicada shrilled in the trees behind the bach, is zithering a harbinger of the greater heat of high summer when the trees would ring with their song.

Conn settled her against his shoulder, holding her gently, without passion. Luce looked down the length of her body, saw the dark olive of his skin contrasted against the paleness of hers and felt a clutch of desire in the pit of her stomach. He had used his body as an instrument of pleasure, forcing from her a response which had shattered any preconceived ideas of ecstasy in a flood of rapturous sensuality. She had always known, in some primitive instinctive part of her, that they would be good together; it was one of the reasons that she had fallen in love with him.

But not the only one. During the long nights she had thought it was passion which kept her tied to him, as it had Nita, but she knew now that passion was only a part of it. Sexually he was all that she could ask for, but he was more to her than a superb lover. Angry though he had been with her, he had been tender and considerate, wooing her with all of her senses until their desire had climaxed in shattering moments of physical and mental union. In the lazy aftermath Luce had realised that she loved him, that she knew him as he knew her; their minds as well as their bodies were attuned.

Now she cursed fate for allowing them to meet two years too soon, for Conn would never believe that she had learned to love him. For two years she had not thought of him, would not have recognised his name, but he had always been with her, as much a part of her as the very cells of her body. Somehow she had learned to love him, to accept him with all his faults and deficiencies. The passionate hero-worship was gone, transmuted by pain and need into a deeper emotion, at once more basic and more realistic. That first love had been wilful and selfish, as all first love must be. What she felt for him now was so essential to her that the mere thought of a life in which he played no part made her shudder.

'Tears?' he said quietly. 'Don't cry, Luce. God knows tears never solved anything. And I'm not worth them.'

'I've done my crying for you,' she returned thickly. 'I'm crying for myself.'

He didn't mock her self-pity 'For that silly little girl?' he said, reading her mind with his usual uncanny accuracy. 'Why cry for her? She enjoyed life; she was too young to know the danger she courted, too innocent to be touched by any of it. It couldn't have lasted, of course. Even if Nita hadn't turned up it wouldn't have lasted, but I thought that by the time we tired of each other you might have acquired some maturity. I couldn't bear the thought of all that ardent, lovely generosity being dragged down into the slime. You'd have gained some sophistication with me, acquired a little caution.'

His words were like a blow to her heart. 'How long did you give us?' she asked under her breath.

Beneath her cheek the smooth hard muscles of his shoulder moved as he shrugged. 'Two or three years. I had no intention of letting you go until you'd learned some discrimination.'

'You—you make Nita and her friends sound like

sharks and wolves,' she said.

'Darling innocent, they were. A hell's kitchen of *nouveaux riches*, hangers-on and decadents. Nita herself had the sort of reputation which even today lifts eyebrows.'

Luce stiffened indignantly. 'It didn't seem to worry you.'

'She was available and she was beautiful, and she was every bit as decadent as her friends,' he said with cold brutality. 'I never claimed to be any better, Luce. But once it had become known that she didn't care a brass farthing for you you would have been lucky to keep any innocence for more than a couple of weeks.'

'I might have had something to say about that!'

He laughed and brought her hard against him, grabbing her wrist when she lifted her hand to fend him off. A pulse drummed in the tender hollow at her elbow; Conn's eyes hardened, then he placed his lips against it. 'Sweetheart, some of her playmates would have had no compunction about raping you, but there are much easier ways to enforce obedience. Booze—or drugs—for the initial occasion, and after that blackmail to ensure that you were available for whoever wanted you.' The ugly words whispered against her skin, teasing even as they repelled her.

'I—don't—believe—you!'

His fingers relaxed. 'No? Well, you're entitled to your opinion, but one of the reasons I married you was that I could see that sort of degradation ahead for you.'

His tones imposed belief. On an exhaled breath she said flatly, 'I see.' And for the first time she did. 'I suppose I should be grateful to you.'

'Gratitude I can do without, but if you feel submerged under the weight of it, you know how to repay me.' He looked into the stormy depths of her eyes and smiled sardonically. 'There were other reasons for our marriage.' His glance dropped to the smooth curve of her breasts, lingered on the flat stomach and the clean taut lines of her thighs. 'You're very beautiful. And you live up to the promises you make, which is more than can be said for some women.'

'How about Nita?' Pain forced the hard sarcasm of her tones, made her draw back as far as she could from him.

Something ugly showed in the darkening depths of his eyes. Without taking his gaze from her body, he pulled her on top of him, and against her throat he murmured, 'Oh, she was an expert, believe me. You've a way to go before you reach her standard.'

Luce pushed with all her might against his shoulders, hating the cold passion she saw in his expression. He was watching her from beneath his lashes, his smile a merciless threat, holding her clamped against him so that she could feel the stirring of his loins and knew that this time there would be no gentleness. She had made him angry and he would make her pay.

'Conn,' she whispered, her breath caught in her throat. 'Please. . . .'

'Begging, Luce? I like to hear you plead; it satisfies my ego.'

'Did you really go to Nita on our wedding night?' She had to know.

'Does it matter?'

She nodded, trying to find an answer in his expression.

'It doesn't matter,' he said slowly. 'What matters is that you assumed I did. If I'd needed any further confirmation of the fact that you felt nothing more for me than a lust you couldn't control, it would have been that.' He pulled her down so that her cheek rested against his shoulder. 'God, I was furious,' he said quietly. 'I used to lie awake at night planning myself any number of interesting revenges. I should have known that you'd put yourself through hell, too.'

'But you went back to her.'

The wide shoulders lifted in a shrug. 'She was there, and you'd made it only too obvious that you were no longer interested. I've never had any taste for rape, and I needed a woman that night.'

Sick horror whitened her face. Huskily, forcing the words past a throat thickened with disgust, she spat, 'You used her! You knew how she felt about you! Even I could see that she was besotted—she'd never have embarked on such a degrading scene if she hadn't been without a will of her own where you were concerned. You're a demon!'

'Her term exactly,' he said, the even tones revealing nothing but boredom. 'She was a high-class slut, Luce, and what she wanted from me was physical gratification, and that was what she got.'

Every muscle in her body tensed, but before she could move, firm fingers on her chin forced her face down to meet his kiss, devouring, swamping anger and disgust in a hot tide of desire. Luce fought him, struggling to break free of the physical and emotional shackles he had imprisoned her in, but he laughed as he subdued her, caressing her until she relaxed, and then kissed her with a drugging sweetness that left her with only his will to guide her.

CHAPTER NINE

A LONG time later, when the sun lay close to the horizon, Conn woke her, his mouth gentle against her shoulder.

Without opening her eyes Luce murmured his name.

'The same,' he drawled, amused. 'Come on, wake up. If I don't get you home the nurses will be out here demanding to know what I've done to their ewe lamb.'

'Hardly,' she retorted drily, discovering that she was still in his arms. Profoundly reluctant though she was to stir, she knew that she would have to move.

'Don't you think so?' His voice moved closer; just brushing her lips with his, he continued, 'Then let's go for a swim.'

Slowly she lifted her lashes, met his amused green gaze. 'Now?'

'Why not? You look as though you could do with something to wake you up. If I take you back looking like that your watchdogs will know immediately how we've spent the afternoon.'

Curiously she asked, 'Wouldn't you like that?'

He grinned. 'Darling heart, they both took one look at me and put me down as an inveterate womaniser. It wouldn't worry me in the least, but you would be embarrassed.'

'You know too much about me,' she complained, hiding a yawn by turning her head into his shoulder.

'So don't ever lie to me again.'

The words hung on the still warm air, flat yet oddly threatening. 'I don't—I haven't,' she stammered after a moment.

Conn turned her face away from the warmth of his shoulder, holding it so that she was forced to meet his cool scrutiny. 'Yes, you have, Luce. You told me that

166

you loved me. I refuse to cloak honest lust with lying emotion. You desire me, you want me, you crave the sensations I can make you feel; leave love to woolly-headed romantics. That way, when it's over, you won't be hurt so badly that you go into hiding to escape.'

His words were like whips across her heart. Through lips paled by pain she said harshly, 'And you—how will you feel? Or have you become such a cynic that nothing can touch you any more?'

'Oh, I can be touched.' His mouth twisted into a smile, cold and meaningful as he looked at her hands and allowed his glance to travel the length of her body. 'I can, indeed. But not by inane appeals to my heart or my better self or my love. It was a crazy gesture, our marriage, so out of character for me that I should have known it was doomed. We'll get each other out of our systems and then I'll go. You're mature enough now to take care of yourself.'

Mockery glinted in the dark eyes at the outrage in her expression. Swiftly rolling away from him, she said in an icy voice, 'You're the most arrogant man I've ever known, and if you think I'm going to spend the next fortnight being treated as one of your mistresses you've another think coming. I want to go home.'

'Why?'

'Because I don't want to stay here with you. Of all the——' She was dragging her clothes on, trembling with rage that masked despair, her fingers clumsy as she yanked up her shorts. 'You really are the limit!' she flung at him. 'Autocratic, cruel, and not nearly as smart as you think you are. I think I hate you!'

Her anger amused him. Without embarrassment he rose and came to stand in front of her, looking into the flushed purity of her features with a keen, too-knowing gaze. 'You look more like the Luce I used to know,' he taunted, and bent his head and kissed her into silence.

Hot tears sprang into her eyes. She felt an ache at the back of her throat and knew that she could not give in to his plans; if she lived with him as his wife for even a few short weeks any subsequent parting would kill her.

Not that she would tell him now, for he was quite capable of refusing to take her back to the flat. And, imprisoned as she was by her love, she didn't think that she could cope with being held against her will.

'Oh—Conn!' she exclaimed hoplessly, holding him against her, touching the jagged scar on his back with loving fingers.

'Sure you want to go back now?'

She nodded, loosening her arms. 'Yes, please.'

As if he sensed the decision she had just made he kissed her again, crushing her already bruised lips beneath his in an embrace which was as brutal as it was devastating. The fountain of desire sprang into life; her hands clenched on his shoulders as he held her against him so that she was left in no doubt as to his need of her.

After long moments he lifted his head, but made no effort to release her. Luce touched her throbbing lips with one hand.

'What was that for?'

Conn shrugged, his lashes hiding all but a predatory gleam while his mouth set in a straight hard line. 'Call it putting my mark on you,' he said curtly. 'For the time being you're mine. You look like a woman who's been thoroughly kissed, and I like it.'

Momentarily hope quickened in her heart, but died stillborn. What he felt for her was possession, not the giving, sharing unselfishness of love. Only a fool would fail to realise that he considered the need he had of her to be a weakness, something to be exorcised.

They drove back to the flat in silence. Once there Luce said calmly, 'I won't come back with you, Conn.'

'Had second thoughts?'

He didn't believe her, she could see that.

'Yes, I'm afraid so.'

'Why?'

Her real reason would amuse him and she had no others ready. To strike back at him eased some of the pain that gripped her, hating as she did the arrogant self-confidence which tilted the corners of his mouth in a smile as he looked at her.

Very coolly she said, 'I don't think I need a fortnight to get you out of my system.'

There was a moment of ominous silence before he said, 'Liar,' and leaned towards her, coming to rest when his mouth was six inches or so away from hers. Very hard and sharp his eyes were, and a muscle tightened along his jawline. 'That pulse is hammering away in your throat,' he stated conversationally, 'and your breath has quickened. If I kissed you now you'd open your mouth to me as you always do, and five minutes after that you'd do anything I wanted. So try again, my wanton wife.'

It took an immense effort of will to shake her head, but she managed it.

'And what's that supposed to mean?' he asked.

'Just that it isn't enough,' she said, her voice flat with the curb she was putting on her emotions. 'I don't want an orgiastic fortnight with a farewell dinner at the end of it.'

'Oh, I usually give a more tangible symbol of my gratitude,' he said softly, viciously.

Tension crackled in the air between them. Luce could feel him willing her towards him and had to summon up all of her hard won strength to resist his silent assault. In the end it was the memory of Nita's abject self-despising face as she had kissed him against her will which gave Luce the will-power to step away.

'I'm not for sale,' she said quietly, turning her head so that he could see only her profile.

'Yes, you are, but your price is a little higher than most others.' He leaned back against the wall, hands in pockets as though he could not trust himself to keep them from her. His anger was tangible, dark and frightening as it beat against her.

After several moments of this silent combat he stated softly, 'I could always make you come with me.'

The savage note threading through his even tones made her shiver. She answered, 'I know, but you would get sick of having to force a response from me. You're not used to it, are you, Conn. Most women find you irresistible.'

'What do you want from me?'

Incredibly she smiled. 'Would you believe me if I said I don't know?'

'Yes, I'd believe you.' He straightened up, saying coldly, 'Well, that's it, then. I'll see you around.'

When the car had gone Luce collapsed in a crumpled heap on the sofa, the tears dripping through her fingers as she wept.

She was still there when Faith came home, pink and salt-bloomed from her day at the beach.

'Fraught, was it?' she asked after one comprehensive glance.

Luce sighed, grateful for her good sense and quiet strength. 'Oh, indeed it was!'

'Tell me to shut up if you want.'

'No, it's all right.' Luce watched as the older woman went into the kitchen. The homely hiss of the tap, the small sounds that signified that Faith was making a pot of tea, soothed and comforted her. 'You know, one of the worst things in life is to get what you want and discover that it's not what you wanted at all. And if that sounds trite, I'm sorry. It's a profound truth.'

'Most trite things are, that's why they become trite.' Faith put cups on to a tray and made a thing of getting the milk from the refrigerator. 'I gather you don't want to talk about it.'

'I don't even know what there is to talk about.'

Luce wasn't deliberately evasive, but she felt immensely weary of the whole disaster that was her marriage. Too much had happened for her brain to cope and she needed nothing so much as a period of quiet reflection to help her to get everything into its proper perspective. Aloud she said drearily, 'He wants me to go and live with him.'

'And you don't want to?'

'Oh yes, I want to.' A small cynical smile touched Luce's mouth. 'I've never been able to resist him. If he'd wanted to take me an hour after we first met I'd have counted the world well lost for lust. He's the one with the scruples.'

Perhaps she wanted to shock Faith, but like Conn, although for different reasons, Faith was unshockable. As she poured the water into the pot the older woman remarked, 'Which should surprise me, of course, except that for all of his ruthlessness he gives the impression of a man who cares very deeply about things. He couldn't write the plays he does if he was a complete cynic. Is it possible that he cares for you?'

'He feels responsible for me. When we met I was living with my stepmother; she wasn't the ideal person to be in charge of a naïve eighteen-year-old. My father died a few months after I'd left school. I spent most of my holidays with my old nurse, but she died too that year, so I was completely alone. I didn't like my stepmother's friends much, but she was kind in an offhand way and she put no restraints on me. I enjoyed discovering London by myself. I used to go to art galleries and museums—oh, I liked my life. And I was always sent up to bed fairly early in the evenings when my stepmother had her big parties.'

'What was her name?'

'Nita Laurenson. She used to be Nita Rothbury.'

Silence, before Faith said in an odd voice, 'Yes, well, I've heard of her, of course. Even over here she figured in the more sensational gossip columns. From the sound of it you were lucky to escape unscathed.'

'Ah, but I didn't,' Luce retorted wryly. 'I ended up marrying Conn, and I'd defy anyone to escape that unscathed.'

'Yes, I see what you mean. Marriage to him would come perilously close to acquiring sophistication in one lesson.'

'Not a particularly easy lesson,' Luce said quietly, accepting a cup of tea with an abstracted air. On the lawn a Californian quail called imperatively to his mate, his absurd crest of feathers giving him a ridiculously regal air. Behind the smaller, drabber hen came seven or eight balls of fluff, the next generation. A smile touched her lips.

'So what do you do now? Go and live with him?'

A shrug lifted Luce's shoulders. 'No. I can't.'

'Have you told him?'

'Yes.'

Faith asked slowly, 'And what did he say to that?'

'I'll see you around.' She smiled drearily at Faith's astonishment. The tea was hot, stronger than normal. Perhaps she needed the extra stimulant, for it tasted good.

'Do you think he's given up on the idea?'

Had he? 'No,' she said. 'No, not Conn. I owe him, and he'll make sure I'll pay.'

Even Faith looked appalled at this blunt statement. 'He sounds a horror,' she began, her dark eyes shrewd as they took in the expression on Luce's face.

'He's a hard man, but he has his own code of honour,' Luce told her, sudden exhaustion sharpening her features. 'He wants me—and he knows I want him. He thinks that it's a weakness—that we should treat it as an affair and let it run its course.' She smiled, cynicism apparent in the weary movement of her lips. 'At the risk of sounding over-dramatic, which he tells me is my usual state, I think I'd die.'

'I suppose people have died of broken hearts, but you've too much character to follow them.' Faith told her briskly. 'You know you're exhausted. Mattie did warn us to be careful of you. Go and have a shower and get into bed and I'll bring your meal in.'

It helped to shower the feel of him from her body; if only she could free herself of his imprint on her heart and her mind so easily! Later, as she pulled on a night-gown, she grimaced at the smudges of deeper colour left on her skin by his hands. His second possession of her had been fiercely demanding and she had responded in kind. Not a gentle lover, Conn, but oh, he knew how to rouse a raging hunger and then sate it with his hands and his mouth and his body, spending his virility with reckless fervour until she was caught up by the force of his passion to a plane of existence where nothing mattered but the sensations he alone could arouse, and the hunger he alone could satisfy.

She had plenty of time to think over those sensations, that hunger, in the following days. It seemed that he had accepted her rejection, for as summer arrived she saw nothing more of him. The wrenched muscles in her body eased back into their usual quietude, the bruises faded, she discovered that she was not carrying his child, and still he stayed away. Luce ate as little as she could without worrying her companions, but even her sun-bathing could not hide the pallor of her face.

And at night she lay, wide eyes staring at the ceiling of the bedroom, trembling with barely suppressed desire as memories rose to the surface of her brain.

Tormented by the sensuous imagery of her fantasies, she twisted and turned, getting little sleep so that she rose each morning heavy-eyed and weary.

The weather became hot; roses bloomed in every garden, their evocative fragrance heavy on the sultry air. The usual realisation that Christmas was not very far away made itself felt, and people began to flock into town, mostly mothers buying gifts for their families before school broke up.

Luce lost weight, but refused to surrender to the needs that were tearing her apart. She would not become an-other of his mistresses, used and then discarded. But the ache within her grew, the hunger and the need, until one day she walked listlessly along the street in her lunch hour and came face to face with Ryan McLeod.

He stopped and greeted her, those hard eyes resting on her face with dispassionate interest.

'Have you been ill?'

Luce looked at him warily. 'I—that is——' She stopped, feeling a perfect fool.

'Come along,' he said calmly, taking her arm and leading her into a nearby restaurant. 'You look as though you could do with feeding up. You've lost at least a half a stone since I saw you last.'

'Not quite.' Wondering wearily why it was her fate to be ordered about by a brace of arrogant males, Luce subsided into a chair, told him what she wanted to eat and waited listlessly while he and the waiter conferred.

A few moments later she was staring into a glass of extremely good sherry, saying, 'I can't drink this. I'll be in no fit state to go back to work.'

'No breakfast?' Ryan lifted an eyebrow. 'Drink it, nevertheless, and tell me why you're trying to starve yourself to death.'

'I'm not.'

'No, you're unhappy and so your appetite has gone. You know, repugnant as it is to me to interfere in anyone else's affairs, I'm going to have to do something about you and that brother-in-law of mine. Sonia is worrying.'

'I'm sorry about that.' Luce eyed him suspiciously, met the ironic humour in his eyes with a faint smile and added impulsively, 'I can see you're the sort of man to hate women bursting into tears all over you, but if you talk about Conn that's j-just what I'll do.'

'I wonder if my reputation could bear it,' he mused. 'You won't, however. Tell me, do you happen to love that arrogant playwright?'

'You've a nerve! The pot calling the kettle black!'

He smiled but asked inflexibly, 'Luce?'

Tears blinded her. She blew her nose, abandoning her

air of sophistication. 'Of course I do! If I didn't I'd take what he's offering and not c-care.'

'And he's offering?'

'A few weeks together to—to get each other out of our systems and then divorce.' She gulped sherry, adding fiercely, 'I could kill him!'

'The feeling is entirely mutual,' he said drily.

Luce's glance flew up to his face, her eyes wide and horrified. 'What do you mean?'

'Last night he had dinner with us. Sonia retired to bed early and after making a determined effort to sink the contents of my whisky bottle Conn mentioned in passing that when next he saw you he had every intention of showing you who was in charge.'

'Was he drunk?'

Ryan shook his head. 'Being ridden by a black dog. I gather that he's unable to write, unable to sleep and, like you, not eating. When I asked the reason he told me, impolitely, to shut my face. Are you going to do the same, Luce?'

'You must admit you're an odd confidante,' she parried, unsure of what she should do.

'The irony strikes me too. Quite frankly it's not my style, but I'm attached to Conn and I have the feeling I could grow to like you.'

'And Sonia is worrying.'

He smiled, appreciating the note of sarcasm in her comment. 'Exactly. Now would you like to tell me exactly why you and he have made such a mess of things?'

Incredibly enough Luce did just that, finding some sort of release in telling this big, uncommunicative man. She spoke rapidly and concisely, without drama, but her voice revealed the shades of her emotions, and while she talked some of the heavy burden that had lain over her began to lift. Her story ended with the coffee. For some minutes Ryan stared into the depths of his cup, frowning slightly.

Then he looked up and said without expression, 'You've had a rough spin of it. What are you going to do now?'

'Go to him, I suppose,' she said hopelessly. 'And hope that he never gets tired of me. Do you think that's what I should do?'

'I never give advice,' he answered smoothly. 'But I'll agree it seems to be the only thing to do. That's if you want to be with him.'

She answered the unspoken question positively. 'Yes. Talking to you has made me realise that there's nothing else I can do. If I'm miserable with him—well, life without him is like walking through a desert.'

'Very well, then.' Ryan looked at his watch. 'I'll be in town all afternoon. I'll collect you from work and take you out.'

'What?' Luce began to stammer. 'B-but I can't—I mean, Graeme has to get someone else—I can't. . . .'

'Luce, do you want things to go on the way they are, each day that passes hardening your attitudes, making it more difficult for either of you to take that first step?'

'No,' she whispered.

'Very well, then.'

'I pity Sonia,' she said darkly as he held her chair for her to get up. 'With a husband like you and a brother like Conn it's a wonder she's got a soul to call her own!'

He smiled down at her, causing a kind of feminine flutter right around the restaurant. 'Welcome to the family.'

At six o'clock that evening he deposited her, clutching the small suitcase of necessities she had packed, at the top of the hill behind the cove. Graeme had been curious about her abrupt request for time off, but his wife was able to take her place and he had let her go with an order to rest and get better.

'Are you sure you don't want me to drive you down?' Ryan asked.

'No.' Luce managed to produce a smile. 'He can't make me go back with you if I walk down. Wish me luck, Ryan.'

'I don't for a moment think you need it.' He smiled, bent and kissed her cheek. 'Off you go!'

He really was a dear, she thought as she made her way carefully down the steep road, smiling at the crassness of such a description.

As well as that inbuilt ruthlessness there was a kindness in Ryan which Conn didn't possess. Except that that wasn't quite fair, either. Conn had been cruel to her, but he had been surprisingly sympathetic, too.

God, I hope I'm doing the right thing, she whispered beneath her breath.

By the time she had reached the bottom of the hill her suitcase weighed a ton and she was so jittery that the scutter of some small animal in the undergrowth beside the road almost made her scream.

It was very still, very hot even beneath the shade of the pohutukawa trees now almost smothered in scarlet and crimson flowers. Even before her call had met with no answer she knew that the beach house was empty. For a moment she hesitated, then shrugged and went in through the wide screen doors, across the shady living room and into the bedroom.

Once there she unpacked, using the empty drawers in the neat built-in dressing table. She had brought mostly shorts and shirts; some wild impulse had led her to pack an exquisite negligee and nightgown, but she bit her lip at the sight of them and hung then up in the wardrobe.

As usual at the end of the day she felt sticky. Normally she had a shower, but the sea beckoned. Her fingers touched a bikini; after a moment's hesitation she left it and when she had stripped off put nothing but a wrap over her skin.

The water was warm, like silk along her limbs, caressing smoothly and wantonly. She stayed in it a long time, swaying gently behind the red rock barrier until at last she made her way across the smooth wet sand.

By the time the sun went down she was worried,
Surely he hadn't taken to roaming the hills aimlessly! A
small smile lifted her spirits. No, she could not imagine
Conn doing anything aimlessly; a more self-directed
man it would be hard to find. So, as he was far too
sensible to drown himself, that meant he had gone out.
Sure enough, a quick peep in the garage revealed it
empty.

Possibly to Sonia's. Which would appeal to Ryan's
sardonic sense of humour. Luce could just imagine him
behaving perfectly normally all evening. In the mean-
time she was hungry. A delve into the refrigerator
revealed cold meat and salads; she didn't realise that it
was the first decent meal she had had in over a week.

By midnight she had fallen asleep twice, waking each
time with a jerk which almost dislocated her neck.

'To hell with this,' she told the sitting-room, and went
into the bedroom, pulled on a nightgown and went to
bed.

And incredibly enough, almost immediately she slept.
A sleep so deep that she remained almost motionless
during the ensuing hours, spread in splendid abandon
across the big bed while the moon made its way across
the sky.

When she woke it was full daylight and Conn was
sitting on the side of the bed, drinking coffee and staring
at the floor as though he wanted to order its immediate
execution.

For a moment Luce couldn't remember where she
was. Her unguarded movement brought him around to
look at her.

'Good morning,' he said formally, every shade of
expression wiped clean from his face.

'Good morning.'

He nodded at the side table. 'I made you coffee.'

'Thank you.'

Much more of this ridiculous formality and she'd tip

the coffee over him. At least it gave her something to do,
so she reached out an arm and took up the mug, blinking at the sunlight as it fell across the floor.

Against it he was a dark silhouette, threatening,
poised to strike. A quick glance revealed a dented pillow
beside her. A flush touched her cheeks and her hand
trembled. To hide it she drank the coffee, totally at a
loss for words, while the thoughts darted around her
brain.

Obviously Conn had no intention of taking what she
had offered, or he would have woken her when he came
to bed. And just where did that leave her? With her
capitulation thrown back in her face, that's where!

'Who brought you here?'

She smiled with irony. 'Ryan.'

'I should have known.' He grinned, almost wolfishly.
'And then went on home, changed and took his wife
and children to the Stewarts' barbecue.'

'Is that where you were?'

He slanted a taunt her way. 'Yes. And he spent the
entire evening giving a terrific impersonation of Ryan
McLeod.'

'You're two of a kind. Poor Sonia!'

'Did he talk you into coming here?' His voice was
level, as though the question was so unimportant it
barely needed an answer.

For a second every muscle in Luce's body tensed.
'No,' she said quietly. 'He gave me a ride, that's all.'

'Good. There's no need for anyone else to be involved
in our affairs.' As if tired of fencing, Conn put his mug
down on the side table, took hers and set it beside his,
then with a purposeful expression asked, 'And just why
did you come, Luce? The truth, now.'

'You won't believe me.'

'Try me.'

She sighed, staring down at her hands. The night had
been hot and all that covered her was a sheet. Against it
her skin was pale gold silk, fine and fragile. 'Because I

want to be with you,' she said tiredly. 'I'm sick of fighting. It's all I've done since you left me on our wedding night. I suppose I love you and I've no pride left.'

'What changed your mind?'

Luce smiled. 'Misery.'

The word was incongruous on the sparkling air, the flat heaviness of it so at odds with the shining morning that it sounded like an obscenity.

Conn shrugged, watching her with his eyes narrowed. 'And are you expecting to live happily ever after?'

God, but he enjoyed hurting her! Her teeth clenched on her lip a moment before she said huskily, 'No. No, I've learned the lesson you set out to teach me. Love is fleeting, enjoy it while you may, etc., etc. I won't plead with you to give me more than you can.' She lifted her lashes to say with a half smile, 'You told me I'd have to crawl. Well, I'm crawling, Conn.'

'Words come easily to you.'

Her pallor increased, was suddenly lost in a flood of scarlet as she realised what he wanted. Not content with her spoken surrender he wanted her to show him in the most basic way of all that she had given in. She looked appealingly up, met a glance which was razor-sharp and merciless and knew that if she failed now she could say goodbye to any future for them together. He had never believed that she loved him, not from the first, and subsequent events had only hardened his attitude. Not without reason; she had been too immature to deal with Nita's revelations in any constructive way, and her running away had been the reaction of a hurt child. He had every reason to consider her naïve, too juvenile to embark on any sort of adult relationship. But he was giving her the chance, if she had courage enough to grasp it.

Nervously she looked at him through her lashes, lips suddenly dry. He was wearing a robe, an old towelling affair belted loosely around the waist, and he was big and virile and tough, totally without the tenderness she craved from him. He did not love her, but he wanted her, and for her that was going to have to be enough.

'What do you want?' she asked.

He smiled. 'Action, Luce. You've always been very vocal about your emotions, but when it comes to translating them into action you don't follow through. Show me how much you love me.'

'O.K.' If she surprised him she would never know, for he still kept that expressionless mask over his features. Very slowly she wriggled beneath the sheet, tugging at the thin cotton of her nightgown, easing it free of her buttocks and above her hips until she could pull it over her head. Then she looked at him and saw the flash of desire he could not hide, and she smiled, carefully concealing her relief. The fact that he had slept beside her last night without waking her had had her worried, but that hunger he couldn't hide told her that whatever his reason it had not been that he no longer wanted her.

'You're too far away,' she said softly.

'Then come closer.'

Oh, he wasn't going to make it easy for her. A spark of anger lit the cool depths of her eyes. She reached out and slid her hand beneath his robe, then grabbed his shoulder and pulled him off balance so that he fell against her. The movement jerked the sheet down and his head lay on her breast.

Luce's heart beat lightly and rapidly. Slowly she put her arms around him and rested her cheek on his thick hair, saying in a shaken voice, 'Conn, I need you so much. Please don't send me back into the darkness without you.'

He moved slightly, sliding his arms around her waist. Against the silken skin of her breasts his mouth made tiny kisses when he spoke. 'Is that what it was for you, Luce? You told me that regaining your memory would hurtle you into that dark abyss.'

'No, it was the knowledge that I'd failed you, that I'd lost you.'

'Oh, God!' The words were wrenched from him. His arms tightened almost unbearably, but he turned his head away from her. He hadn't shaved and the dark shadow of his beard seared across her breast, but she said nothing, holding him close against her so that her heart fluttered beneath his cheek.

'If I take you now I'll never let you go,' he told her harshly. 'Do you think you could stand a lifetime of it, Luce? I can't promise to be anything other than fiercely possessive and I'll probably breathe fire down the throat of any man who so much as smiles at you, but I'll do my best to make you happy.'

'Just being with you will make me happy.'

He was very still, and then said slowly, 'For how long, Luce? Until passion wanes as it will, as it must?'

Bewildered by his change in attitude, she yet knew that what she said now could well be the cornerstone of their life together. Somehow she must make him see what was in her heart.

'If it fades, then surely there'll be other things to take its place,' she whispered. 'If we share a life, doesn't that make bonds of a different sort but just as strong? I want to have your children, Conn, to see them grow, to make the kind of home for them that neither you nor I had.' Tears came to her eyes. She felt them spill over, but dared not relax her hold on him in case he took it as a rejection. Turning her head, she buried her face into his hair, saying in a voice muffled by emotion, 'But I don't mind if you don't want that sort of life. I just want to be with you. Please! I only feel alive when you are with me.'

He said nothing, and after a moment of unbearable tension she said, 'I know you don't love me——'

'Luce, you stupid little fool! I fell in love with you the first time I saw you,' he groaned, lifting his head to look at her. 'Like a boy of twenty. Helplessly—head over heels and fathoms deep.'

She stared, unable to believe her ears. 'But you never

said—you didn't——'

'Of course I didn't,' Conn smiled, irony and self-contempt mixed. 'Move over.'

Luce knew that she should be happy. Had he not just told her what she had longed to know but resigned herself to never hearing? But even as he slid between the sheets, abandoning his robe on the way, and took her in his arms, she could only feel a tired astonishment.

'Why?' she asked. 'Why didn't you tell me?'

'Because you felt no such emotion for me.'

'But I did—I did!'

He shook his head, smoothing away the frown lines on her forehead with a gentle finger. 'No, you didn't. You jumped head first into your first bout of physical attraction. I'm not blaming you for it; at eighteen that's about all that you were capable of feeling. You were wilful and ardent and unscrupulous and utterly enchanting, and I wanted you more than I'd ever wanted anything in my life before. But I wouldn't have married you then if it hadn't been for the ménage you were in and your wholly ruthless way of dealing with your frustration. If you'd had a normal family I'd have hung around until your attraction had deepened into love, possibly after two or three love affairs. Unfortunately I couldn't afford the time.'

Luce still couldn't believe him, though his explanation made so much clear. 'But you were Nita's lover,' she said in a small voice.

The muscles in his shoulder moved as he shrugged. 'Until I met you.'

'But—she said—that you still were, and you didn't say no.'

'Try and understand just how things were. Somehow I had to cope with my emotions for you; I'd never felt like that before and more than anything I wanted to marry you and make you safe, only I knew that it wasn't fair to you. You could—probably would—fall out of love as easily as you fell in love. At eighteen one's emotions are hardly stable. And it would have killed me to let you go. Then there was Nita. Apart from the fact that she was your stepmother she had been generous and undemanding. I didn't want to hurt her more than was necessary.'

Luce nodded, seeing for the first time just how she had contributed to the disastrous course of their marriage. 'So I threatened to behave like a promiscuous little fool and you came over all chivalrous,' she said, burrowing her head into his chest to cool her hot cheeks.

Conn laughed softly as he stroked her arms and neck and cheek. 'Yes. When Nita appeared like the wicked fairy on our wedding night I'd had enough, especially as I could see that you believed every word she said. So I behaved as badly as I could, feeling that I'd got into a situation from which we'd all emerge losers.'

'Which was what happened, thanks to my idiocy.'

'No, mine,' he said roughly. 'I knew you weren't capable of anything more than a kind of hero-worship with sexual overtones, but it still hurt like hell when you behaved like an adolescent.' He swung her close to him, crushing her against him as he said through clenched teeth, 'I don't suppose you'll ever know how it felt to make love to you and get no response. If I hadn't gone out I'd have raped you. At least I still had sense enough to know that if I did that I'd have destroyed any chance of making our marriage work.'

'I ached with frustration,' she said, kissing his shoulder and throat, pressing her open mouth against the warm smooth skin until he began to tremble and caught her hair and held her head away.

'In a moment,' he said thickly. 'This time I want it to be perfect, for both of us, free from any taint of the past.'

She smiled, looking at him from beneath lowered lashes and ran her hand down his side, coming to rest on his hip, delighting in the sudden tension of his body at her touch.

'Witch,' he muttered, holding her still. 'No, I mean it. Is there anything else you want to know?'

'What were you doing with Nita when she was killed?' Her fingers traced out the ugly scar.

'We were both at a party. Oh, not together. She was high, marijuana, I think, so I drove her home. That was all. I didn't go to her on our wedding night—I lied to you about that. I walked the streets, finally decided to come back and tell you the truth. When I got there you'd gone, and I couldn't find you.'

Something in the way he spoke told her of the desolation he had felt, and she gave a choked sob. 'I thought I was the only one to suffer. Oh, Conn, I'm so sorry for everything!'

'I'm not.' He kissed her forehead, holding her close in a comforting embrace. 'God knows, it was as much my fault as yours. I could have saved us both a lot of pain if I'd been open with you. I've a nasty temper, my love, and I can't promise to change overnight.'

'I don't want you to change.' Luce rested her head against his chest, surprised that lying together like this, like lovers, they could yet be talking so quietly, so earnestly. She could feel the smooth warmth of his body against hers, the strength and the faint tangy scent of him, and although she was acutely conscious of his leashed passion she was relaxed. Soon they would make love and she would know again the singing ecstasy, the uprushing fountain of desire which for too short a time freed them from the immense loneliness of humankind. But now was not the time, now it was enough to talk and lift the burdens of the past, to feel safe and warm and loved.

'I like you the way you are,' she said, smiling yet more serious than she had ever been before in her life. 'I love you the way you are. But why were you so—so aloof when I finally did remember? You told me that you felt nothing for me but lust, and that I owed you myself for all your trouble. Why?'

'I wanted you to love me. I knew as soon as I saw you again that the physical magic was as strong as ever.' His hands around her face were gentle, but he spoke with a harshness that revealed how much pressure he was under. 'You have no idea how much it hurt to see you fight me, the fear and anger in your eyes—yet that, and the desire you couldn't hide, gave me hope. I dreaded the return of your memory—it seemed that there was an even chance you could wake up loathing me. So I kissed you and made love to you, trying to make it impossible for you to resist me.'

She smiled against his shoulder, her expression mischievous. 'You were wicked.'

'Not nearly as wicked as I could have been.' Conn sighed, touching her throat and breast with a gentle hand. 'But when you did regain your memory, we seemed to have gone backwards. You hated me and despised yourself. I gave you time to get over the shock and we made love, but I knew we still weren't out of the woods. I loved you more than I believed it possible to love a woman; you wanted me but you hated me, seeing your desire as the sort of physical subjugation you despised in Nita.'

'And Jolie.' She should not have been astounded at how well he read her mind, but she was, lifting her head from his shoulder so that she met the hot green of his gaze. 'How did you know?'

'I know the way you think,' he told her wryly. His hand swept the contours of her body, fiercely possessive against her skin.

Luce winced, but her body knew its master, moving sinuously against him in open provocation, revelling in the instant tension she aroused in him. He bent his head but didn't kiss her until she moved, angry at the taunt in his gaze. She pulled his head down, teasing his mouth open with hers, using all the sexuality he had brought to life to force him to lose control.

The kiss was painful yet satisfying, a dark merging of mouths that was a seal of possession for them both, a promise for the future. And still his hands moved, reinforcing their mastery of her responses as they explored.

'I'm hurting you,' he said thickly.

'I don't care.'

He smiled, but his touch gentled and after a moment he said with harsh distinctness, 'Well, that's it. I wanted your surrender in every way. It was a test, if you like. I felt that the only way for you to prove you loved me was for you to sink your pride completely. It was a gamble, but I won. You came here last night. When I came in you were sprawled across my bed. I——' he stopped, lowering his head to rest his face in the warmth of her neck. After a moment he resumed in muffled tones, 'My sweet joy, I could have wept with relief. I was bloody tired, so I got in beside you and you turned and cuddled against me, and it seemed the most natural thing in the world to go to sleep to the sound of your breathing and the warmth of your body against mine.'

There was a long silence, before Luce said huskily, 'Yet you were beastly to me when you woke me.'

'As always, morning brought doubts. I had to turn the screw a bit, just to make sure that you knew what you were doing.'

He released her, turning away to fumble in the drawer of the small table by the bed. Luce lay still, hardly breathing, shaken to her depths by the naked need in his voice and face. For a moment the tough, arrogant lines of his face had altered. He had looked vulnerable. It seemed a contradiction in terms. Conn—vulnerable? Yet he had been, and she had known then just how much he loved her. And the wonder and glory of it frightened her and exhilarated her and made her so humble that she could have wept.

'Here,' he said. In his hand was the plain gold wedding ring he had given her two years ago. The morning sun caught it as he slid it on. 'When I pushed that ruby one on your finger, that first time in the shop, I hoped it might stir a memory,' he said. 'I liked the look of it, and as we didn't get an engagement ring I bought it.'

'Where is it?' Her voice was thick, so low in her throat that she cleared it.

He had kept them together. 'If you don't like it we can get another,' he said.

'I love it.' The tears gathered as she bent her head and kissed his hand, laying her cheek against the lean strength of it in a gesture which revealed how incredibly moved she was.

'Oh, God, Conn, never leave me again. I couldn't bear it.'

He leaned back into the pillows, pulling her so that she lay against him, his expression darkly intent as he traced the gentle curves of her body with a loving finger.

'Never again,' he muttered. 'I promise, never again.'

He kissed the ring and her finger; his mouth moved to her throat, touched the pulse there and moved slowly, purposefully, over her shoulders. Luce felt the sweet tension stir again deep with her, the rise of desire. His action had displaced the sheet and she drew her breath as the lean strong hands moved across the whiteness of her skin.

'I love you,' she whispered, her fingers caressing the broad shoulders.

'I'd die for you.' Conn lifted his head, his expression taut with passion, warmed by the love he no longer hid. As his mouth took hers she groaned, her hands fiercely pulling him against her. She wanted only to give, to recompense him for the lost years and the pain, and as always happens, in the giving she received as much again.

Harlequin Plus

A WORD ABOUT THE AUTHOR

Robyn Donald is a native New Zealander. She grew up on a dairy farm, met her future husband when she was fifteen, went to Auckland to train as a teacher and then came home to be married.

After the birth of a son, the family moved to Auckland. A little lonely and housebound as she awaited the birth of her daughter, Robyn began the first tentative steps that set her on the path to writing. Her first attempt was, she says, "appallingly bad." But she was determined to keep at it.

Another move took the family to the far north of New Zealand. Robyn returned to teaching but still found time to write; with her husband's encouragement she submitted a manuscript entitled *Bride at Whangatapu*. It was accepted and became Harlequin Presents #232, published in 1978.

For reference, Robyn keeps a file of clippings, jottings of ideas, photographs and a diary, which, she laughingly says, "is useful in my work as well as for settling family arguments!"

Harlequin ✦ *Salutes...*

JANET DAILEY

...with 6 more of her bestselling Presents novels!

13 The Matchmakers (#264)
14 For Bitter or Worse (#267)
15 Green Mountain Man (#272)
16 Six White Horses (#275)
17 Summer Mahogany (#279)
18 The Bride of the Delta Queen (#284)

Once again Harlequin is proud to salute Janet Dailey, one of the world's most popular romance authors. Now's your chance to discover 6 of Janet Dailey's best—6 great love stories that will intrigue you, captivate you and thrill you as only Harlequin romances can!

Available in May wherever paperback books are sold, or through
Harlequin Reader Service:

In the U.S.
1440 South Priest Drive
Tempe, AZ 85281

In Canada
649 Ontario Street
Stratford, Ontario N5A 6W2

Take these 4 best-selling novels FREE

That's right! FOUR first-rate Harlequin romance novels by four world renowned authors, FREE, as your introduction to the Harlequin Presents Subscription Plan. Be swept along by these FOUR exciting, poignant and sophisticated novels . . . . Travel to the Mediterranean island of Cyprus in **Anne Hampson**'s "Gates of Steel" . . . to Portugal for **Anne Mather**'s "Sweet Revenge" . . . to France and **Violet Winspear**'s "Devil in a Silver Room" . . . and the sprawling state of Texas for **Janet Dailey**'s "No Quarter Asked."

Harlequin Presents...

The very finest in romantic fiction

Join the millions of avid Harlequin readers all over the world who delight in the magic of a really exciting novel. SIX great NEW titles published EACH MONTH! Each month you will get to know exciting, interesting, true-to-life people . . . . You'll be swept to distant lands you've dreamed of visiting . . . . Intrigue, adventure, romance, and the destiny of many lives will thrill you through each Harlequin Presents novel.

Get all the latest books before they're sold out!

As a Harlequin subscriber you actually receive your personal copies of the latest Presents novels immediately after they come off the press, so you're sure of getting all 6 each month.

Cancel your subscription whenever you wish!

You don't have to buy any minimum number of books. Whenever you decide to stop your subscription just let us know and we'll cancel all further shipments.